This Book Belongs to:

_____

_____

Animal Encyclopedia Activity Journals

JURASSIC ANIMALS

MORE THAN 150 PAGES OF JURASSIC ANIMAL
FACTS & FUN ACTIVITIES

JUAN CARLOS ALONSO & GREGORY S. PAUL

© 2019 Quarto Publishing Group USA Inc.
Artwork © Juan Carlos Alonso
Select images used for design elements and activities © Shutterstock

First published in 2019 by Walter Foster Jr., an imprint of The Quarto Group.
26391 Crown Valley Parkway, Suite 220, Mission Viejo, CA 92691, USA.
T (949) 380-7510 **F** (949) 380-7575 **www.QuartoKnows.com**

Walter Foster Jr. titles are also available at discount for retail, wholesale, promotional, and bulk purchase. For details, contact the Special Sales Manager by email at specialsales@quarto.com or by mail at The Quarto Group, Attn: Special Sales Manager, 100 Cummings Center, Suite 265D, Beverly, MA 01915, USA.

ISBN: 978-1-60058-850-1

Written by Juan Carlos Alonso and Gregory S. Paul
Illustrated by Juan Carlos Alonso
Project editing, puzzles, and activities by Elizabeth T. Gilbert

Printed in China
10 9 8 7 6 5 4 3 2 1

For Betty and Dalí, your undying support and endless inspiration make everything worthwhile. Love, Juan Carlos

Table of Contents

Foreword

Matthew T. Mossbrucker

Director & Chief Curator

Morrison Natural History Museum, Morrison, Colorado

Jurassic! For kids (and some adults), this word immediately brings to mind images of giant dinosaurs crashing and smashing their way through a dim, primeval forest while a volcano explodes somewhere in the distance. When I was a kid reading dinosaur books like this one, I was surprised to learn that the Jurassic wasn't a *where* like that imaginary forest, but a *when*.

The word "Jurassic" refers to a special time in the history of our planet, beginning 201 million years ago and ending about 145 million years ago. Our planet is old—really, really old. The Earth is so old that we use words to tell time instead of clocks. Giving names to periods from Earth's history helps us chart time, similar to how a calendar helps us talk about when events happened in the past. "When were you born?" my kids ask me, and I say "May of 1979." When we talk about dinosaurs, they ask "When did Stegosaurus live?" and I say "The Jurassic."

The Jurassic lasted for so long that it is broken up into smaller pieces, kind of like a year is broken down into months. The Jurassic is first divided into three big chunks of time called "Early," "Middle," and "Late." Then it is divided again into even smaller time-chunks with formal names like "Oxfordian," as well as ten others. Fifty-six million years is a long time, and no dinosaur lived for the entire Jurassic period.

Fossils are the remains of living things preserved in stone that was once mud or sand. Dinosaur fossils are only found in specific layers of rock that were deposited as sand and dirt during a small part of the Jurassic. These remains help us learn about what lived during the Jurassic.

Some of the most famous dinosaurs lived during the Late Jurassic. Fossils of the spike-tailed Stegosaurus and the fearsome birdlike Allosaurus are found together in western North America, along with the giant dino-cousins, Apatosaurus and Brontosaurus. Not all dinosaurs lived at the same time or even in the same place. The oldest dinosaurs of the Early Jurassic are remarkable, like the ancestor of Stegosaurus, the armor-studded Scelidosaurus from England.

The first Jurassic dinosaur fossils found were named Megalosaurus in 1824. They were from Middle Jurassic age rocks in England. Megalosaurus fossils helped define what it means to be a dinosaur. Middle Jurassic fossils remain elusive to this day. In fact, modern paleontologists are still discovering new animals and plants from extinct streams and ponds that once offered Jurassic dinosaurs a drink.

As you read this book, think about each dinosaur and what its life might have been like. Take a trip to your library and read as many dinosaur books as you can find. Visit your local museum and learn more about the dinosaurs that might have lived in your own backyard.

Introduction

Come along with us on a journey deep into the Earth's history, to a time long before the first humans ever existed. A time when giants roamed the Earth and reptiles ruled the skies. A time of absolute beauty and extreme danger—this is the Late Jurassic.

245 Million Years Ago

208 Million Years Ago

Permian

TRIASSIC PERIOD

During the Permian period, the Earth's landmasses were connected in a supercontinent called "Pangaea." Life forms were diverse, but big changes in the climate and environment caused mass extinctions at the end.

Dinosaurs first appeared in the Triassic period. During this block of time, Earth's plate tectonic activity caused the land to shift, and Pangaea began to pull apart into different pieces.

We are now about 150 million years away from the Earth as we know it. Standing in lush green surroundings, you take a deep breath and notice how thick the air is with humidity. The unique smell of wet and decomposing plant matter overwhelms you as the sound of insects rings endlessly in your ears. The air is stifling hot, making it exhausting to get around. The Late Jurassic does not welcome visitors.

Mesozoic Era

162 Million Years Ago

145 Million Years Ago

65 Million Years Ago

JURASSIC PERIOD

CRETACEOUS PERIOD

LATE JURASSIC

The Jurassic period is the middle portion of the Mesozoic era, better known as "the age of reptiles." The Late Jurassic was home to some of the most fascinating animals, including the animals in this book!

During the Cretaceous period, the continents continued to shift, and rodents and flowering plants appeared. Dinosaurs of the Cretaceous period include Tyrannosaurus rex (T. rex), Velociraptor, and Triceratops. This period ended with the extinction of the dinosaurs.

During the Late Jurassic, the Earth is experiencing significant changes, including volcanic activity due to shifting tectonic plates. The once supercontinent, Pangaea, is now divided into four landmasses consisting of South America and Africa, Western Europe and Asia, Australia and Antarctica, and North America.

The eruptions from volcanoes along with greenhouse gasses are raising temperatures worldwide, several degrees warmer than in modern times. Because of this, there are no polar ice caps, leading to extremely high sea levels. The two largest bodies of water, the Pacific Ocean and the Tethys Ocean, take up 80 percent of the Earth's surface, while the Atlantic Ocean is just beginning to appear as a small inland sea. The world is a warm, wet, and tropical place—the perfect environment for plant and animal development.

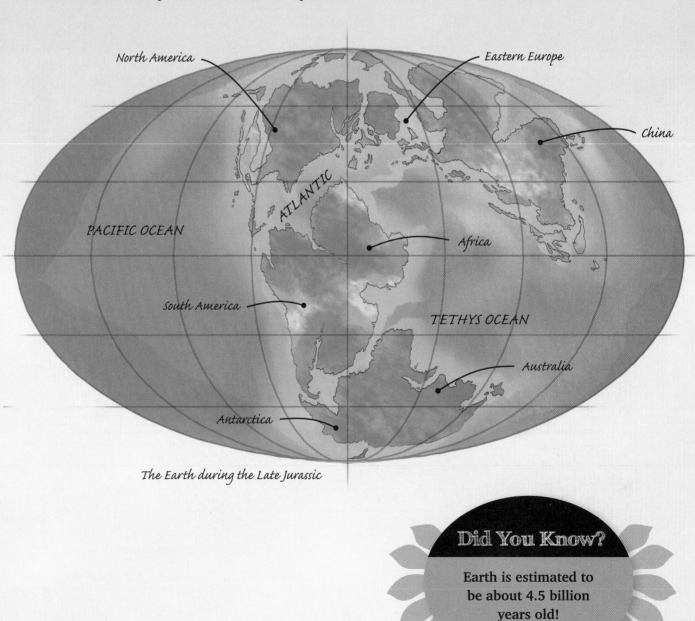

The Earth during the Late Jurassic

Did You Know?

Earth is estimated to be about 4.5 billion years old!

Fossil Hot Spots

Several areas across the world offer easy access to sedimentary rock and ash beds formed during the Late Jurassic, which makes them ideal for fossil discovery. Learn about the most important hot spots below!

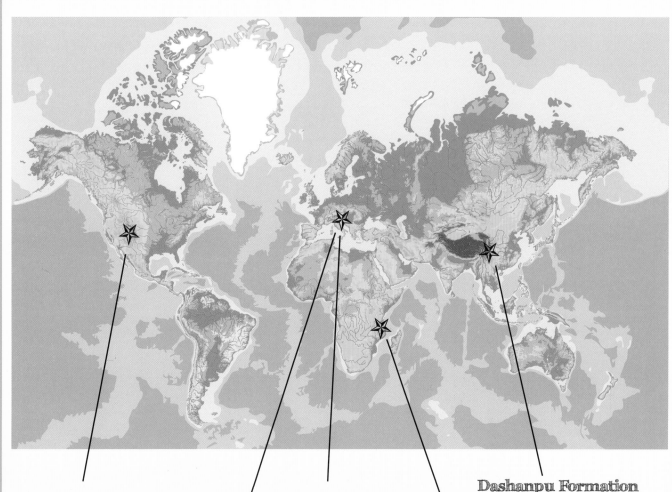

The Morrison Formation
Located in the western United States, this sedimentary rock unit runs from New Mexico to Montana. It is rich with dinosaur fossils, including those of the Allosaurus and Stegosaurus.

The Jura Mountains
This formation is located along the border of France and Switzerland. It is the site of the longest track of sauropod footprints yet discovered.

Dashanpu Formation
This site in south-central China has provided glimpses of the late Jurassic, including fossils belonging to Yangchuanosaurus.

Solnhofen Formation
This limestone formation in southern Germany is where Archaeopteryx was discovered— including a well-preserved impression of its feather.

Tendaguru Formation
This formation in Tanzania has been the site of many fossil discoveries, including Giraffatitan and Kentrosaurus.

Around you the landscape is composed of tall conifer trees like the Araucaria (see fig. a) and Ginkgo trees. Low-lying club mosses (see fig. b) and Neocalamites, or horsetail plants (see fig. c), stem from and around freshwater ponds and creeks. Ferns and cycads, like Otozamites (see fig. d), dominate as ground cover and low trees. Everywhere you look you are surrounded by greenery. This greenery fuels the growth of enormous plant-eating dinosaurs.

Some dinosaur species are rapidly evolving larger in a race to outgrow the predators that feed on them, some reaching lengths of over 100 feet. As groups of dinosaurs, such as the sauropods, evolve into larger species, so do their predators. Animals like Allosaurus and Torvosaurus are becoming apex predators reaching over 30 feet in length, armed with weaponry designed to dispatch their prey quickly and efficiently. While some herbivorous dinosaurs are finding safety in size, others are beginning to develop armor or speed as a way to elude the jaws of predators.

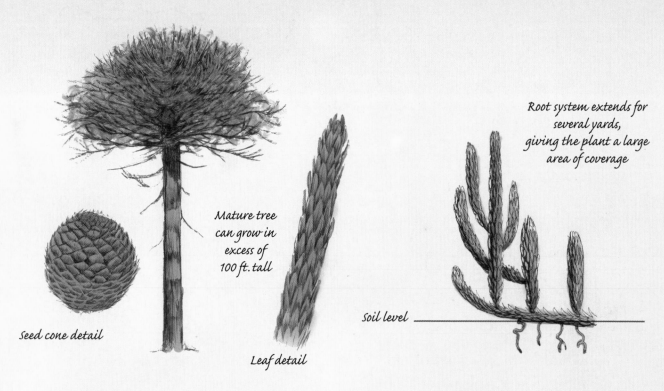

Mature tree can grow in excess of 100 ft. tall

Seed cone detail

Leaf detail

Root system extends for several yards, giving the plant a large area of coverage

Soil level

Figure a. Araucaria Tree

Figure b. Club Moss

Danger comes in all sizes, as smaller predators are filling evolutionary niches and becoming specialized hunters. Gliding through the air from trees is becoming a new means of hunting for the smaller theropod dinosaurs. This method will soon give rise to the first true birds. But for now, pterosaurs, or "flying reptiles," are the undisputed rulers of the sky. Though diminutive in size, their adaptations and ability for flight are unmatched by any other vertebrates.

Continue along on our journey as we dive deeper into the wildlife of the Late Jurassic than ever before, coming face to face with everything from early mammals to super predators. In this book, you will discover how some dinosaurs developed techniques for hunting while others used new adaptations for self-defense. Page by page, you'll see a first-hand, intimate account of what it was like to stand ankle-high next to the largest group of animals to walk the Earth. These animals towered over our closest relatives—the early mammals—as they began to stake their claim in a world dominated by dinosaurs. This is the Late Jurassic as never seen before.

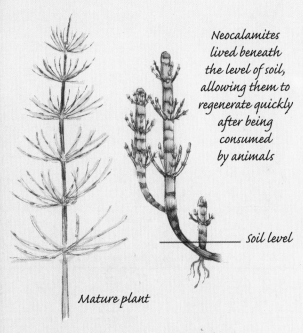

Neocalamites lived beneath the level of soil, allowing them to regenerate quickly after being consumed by animals

soil level

Mature plant

Figure c. Neocalamites

Mature plant

Leaf detail

Figure d. Otozamites

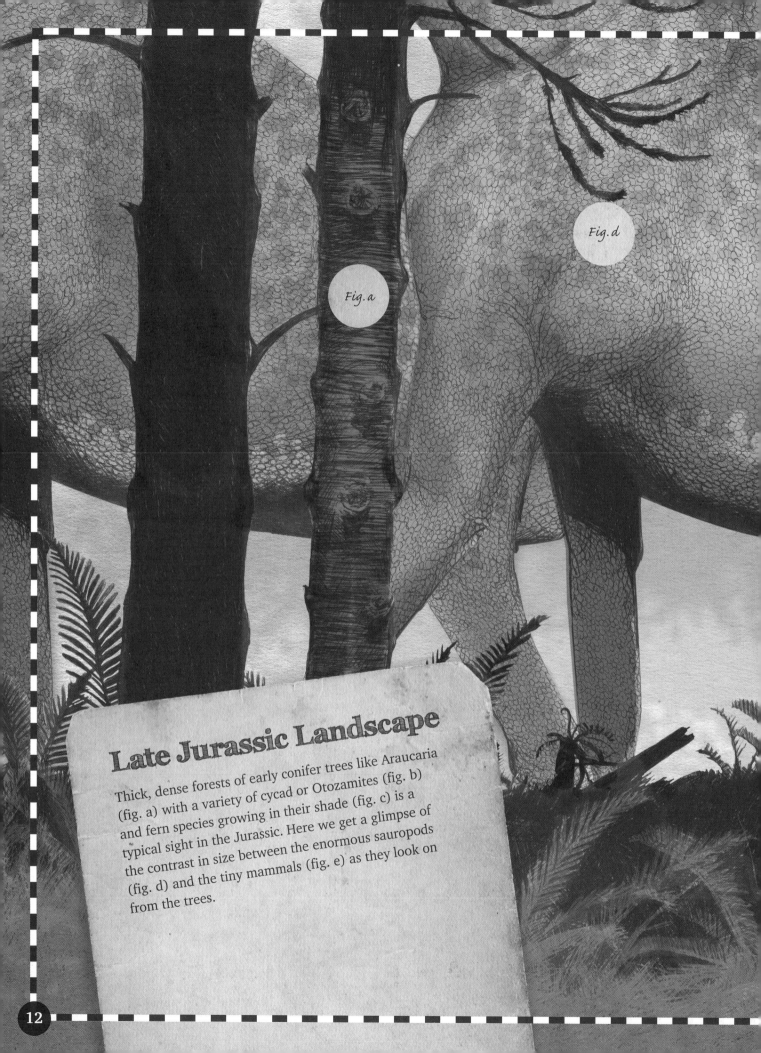

Fig. a

Fig. d

Late Jurassic Landscape

Thick, dense forests of early conifer trees like Araucaria (fig. a) with a variety of cycad or Otozamites (fig. b) and fern species growing in their shade (fig. c) is a typical sight in the Jurassic. Here we get a glimpse of the contrast in size between the enormous sauropods (fig. d) and the tiny mammals (fig. e) as they look on from the trees.

Fig. e

Fig. b

Fig. c

Theropods

Our journey begins in search of the largest predators to ever walk the earth: the theropods. You find yourself standing on a vast flood plain. The ground is dry, but in a few months, during the rainy season, this area will be submerged underwater. For now, it serves as an open path for both predators and prey to travel freely. Beneath you lies a mosaic of footprints, including small and large three-toed impressions. The largest of these footprints is 1.5 feet from toe to heel. This, without a doubt, belongs to a large theropod. It is freshly made.

The cold feeling of fear runs through you as you realize the dinosaur could be anywhere. Without thinking twice, you begin to run for cover toward the nearest cluster of trees. You can feel its presence behind you, but cannot force yourself to turn around. Within the relative safety of the trees, you keep running toward the densest part of the woods, where you hope it cannot follow you. From the shelter of a thick trunk, you slowly turn to see your pursuer.

9 feet

6 feet

3 feet

Standing around 10 feet tall, with its head hung low to avoid detection, the theropod gradually cocks its head to one side to get a better look at you. It raises its snout and sniffs the air. The look in its eye, one of focus and determination, reminds you of a bird of prey. There is no question: You are being hunted. With small horns above its eyes and dagger-sized, hooked claws hanging from its thick arms, this animal instills the kind of fear no other living animal can. You can feel your heartbeat through your chest as it cautiously steps closer and again sniffs the air. It doesn't recognize your scent, and it doesn't know what to make of you. With a loud snort, it turns its back and calmly walks away as its long tail follows. You have just survived an encounter with a Late Jurassic theropod.

Theropods were a group of dinosaurs that included some of the largest and most fearsome carnivorous animals to ever exist. Though some were truly scary, in reality, many were no larger than a turkey.

Theropods were a very diverse group of animals known for being bipedal, meaning they used two legs for walking, and most were known for being carnivorous. Some theropods developed instincts for caring for their young and finding mates, much like birds do today. As a matter of fact, theropod dinosaurs have not technically become extinct, as some evolved into modern birds.

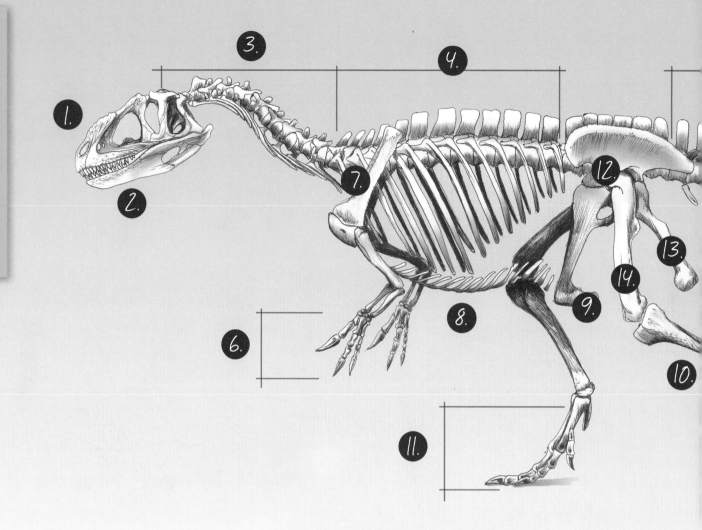

Theropods of the Late Jurassic

By the Late Jurassic, several species of theropods had reached unprecedented size. This trend called "gigantism" was only the beginning. Soon super predators reaching 40 to 55 feet in length began to dominate the Earth in the following period: the Cretaceous. But in the Jurassic, 30- to 35-foot-long theropods were at the top of the food chain. Many of them had hands built like the talons of an eagle, with a razor-sharp thumb claw over 9 inches long. Because prey animals were becoming larger, some theropods may have developed hunting techniques such as pack hunting, where several individuals worked together to bring down larger prey.

The smaller theropods were making their mark as well. Species like *Archaeopteryx lithographica* and *Yi qi* developed an ingenious method of hunting for food. By gliding down from trees, they captured prey unreachable by any other means, as well as evaded predators. They were the first airborne dinosaurs. Later as these species evolved to become skilled fliers, they led the way to the first true birds. Other species like *Ornitholestes hermanni* and *Guanlong wucaii* were carving out a place of their own between both giant and small hunters. Swift and agile, they were proficient at running down prey generally too large for the small theropods, as well as the smaller theropods themselves.

15.

Anatomy of a Late Jurassic Theropod Skeleton

1. skull	6. manus	11. pes
2. mandible	7. scapula	12. ilium
3. cervical vertebrae	8. gastralia	13. ischium
4. dorsal vertebrae	9. pubis	14. femur
5. caudal vertebrae	10. tibia and fibula	15. chevrons

Number Maze

Help the theropod reach his prey! Work your way through the maze in order from 1 to 10. You can move up, down, left, right, or diagonally!

ANSWER ON PAGE 156

2	3	4	2	2
1	7	3	9	3

1	2	2	3	1	4	8
4	3	4	4	5	6	5
5	1	10	7	6	9	10
7	2	1	8	4		
10	4	6	9	10		

Dino Decoding

Use the alphabet key to find the answer to the question below!

ANSWER ON PAGE 156

A @	H ^	O -	V 6
B !	I &	P |	W <
C 9	J)	Q \	X 1
D $	K (	R ?	Y 8
E 5	L *	S /	Z #
F %	M +	T 2	
G ~	N =	U >	

In 1841, English scientist and fossil expert Sir Richard Owen coined the word "dinosaur" to describe these ancient beasts. This term is Greek for what two words?

__ __ __ __ __ __ __ __   __ __ __ __ __ __
2 5 ? ? & ! * 5   * & # @ ? $

If you could be any dinosaur, which one would you be? Use the alphabet on this page to write your answer in code here!

Theropod Word Search

As you continue to learn about theropods, remember these important words! They are also buried in the word search below. Can you find them all?

ANSWERS ON PAGE 156

- ☐ Adaptations
- ☐ Bipedal
- ☐ Carnivorous
- ☐ Claws
- ☐ Evolution
- ☐ Gigantism
- ☐ Hunter
- ☐ Predator
- ☐ Scales
- ☐ Sharp teeth

```
H P T I L I Z G Q V N A Y L I B Q C W Y
S U Z D O G V I V F M D W Y U I A D D W
Z N N J D B E G F T D A N H Y R I Y E A
G Z E T S H T A P K K P K N Q I O U V I
U W C B E O U N F L R T T W C F T J O Z
M S A C M R B T P N B A Y X F P S J L H
K G V A O Y C I H N R T J C D S Y S U V
Q Z U R R J D S I D A I S O M B J H T O
B W H N W Y K M E J W O E P U Y L A I G
I L A I X T N D W N F N U F U D G R O Y
P P W V N L R G A E V S G P S V F P N O
E E N O H E U H I Z J A W K W W R T X Q
D I D R H J J M D R M T V M F Z J E B S
A W J O X F X B L H E M U E M E Z E I K
L T N U W T P R E D A T O R A L V T E J
X Z G S W S H D I Z I Y J V T C N H R A
D Y E S Y J F U B L S H Y E V K K W T G I
K Z D U T A Q V E K E V T N E L V B R X
D S C A L E S M B F C W B Y N Q N E C D
Y C L A W S A V E R A M U X N R Z F H J
```

19

Allosaurus fragilis

Location Observed: *Colorado and Utah, United States*

Family: *Allosauridae*

Length: *30 feet (9 meters)*

Height: *9.5 feet (3 meters)*

Weight: *1.7 tons*

Temperament: *Aggressive*

Coarse, scaly skin

Long, curved neck

Powerful arms with three claws for grasping prey

Narrow, slender body

Long, strong legs

Did You Know?

Allosaurus was one of the largest predators of the Late Jurassic.

Two pronounced
crests with horns

Ear opening

Developed
olfactory sense

Narrow, serrated teeth designed
to slice through flesh

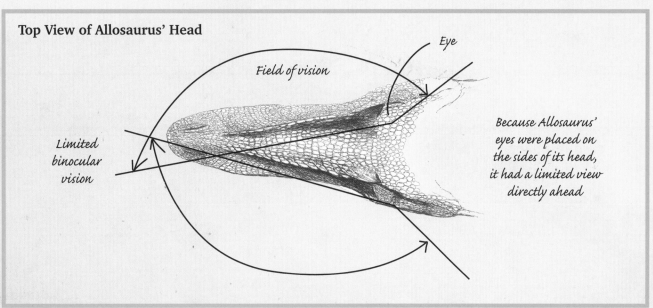

Top View of Allosaurus' Head

Eye

Field of vision

Limited
binocular
vision

Because Allosaurus'
eyes were placed on
the sides of its head,
it had a limited view
directly ahead

True or False?

Dinosaur skulls are made of delicate, thin bone that is easily broken or crushed.

ANSWER ON PAGE 156

Allosaurus had an impressive bite. Its jaws were able to open over 90 degrees, allowing it to attack much larger prey, including sauropods.

Equally as dangerous as its bite, Allosaurus' forelimbs contained enormous claws used to dispatch prey or act as meat hooks to seize larger animals

9-inch-long thumb claw

Did You Know?

Allosaurus means "different lizard" because its vertebrae were different from other known dinosuars when it was discovered.

A young sauropod falls prey to a pack of Allosaurs. Using its flexible jaws and grasping claws, Allosaurus slows down and eventually brings the sauropod's neck closer to the ground.

Create Your Own Dinosaur

Small, tall, scary, or just plain strange, dinosaurs could be a lot of different things! If you could make your own imaginary dinosaur, what would it look like? How would it move, and what would it eat? On the following pages, use the space to draw (and name!) your own species. You can even mix and match from the columns for wacky ideas! Choose one head, one body, and one tail for inspiration.

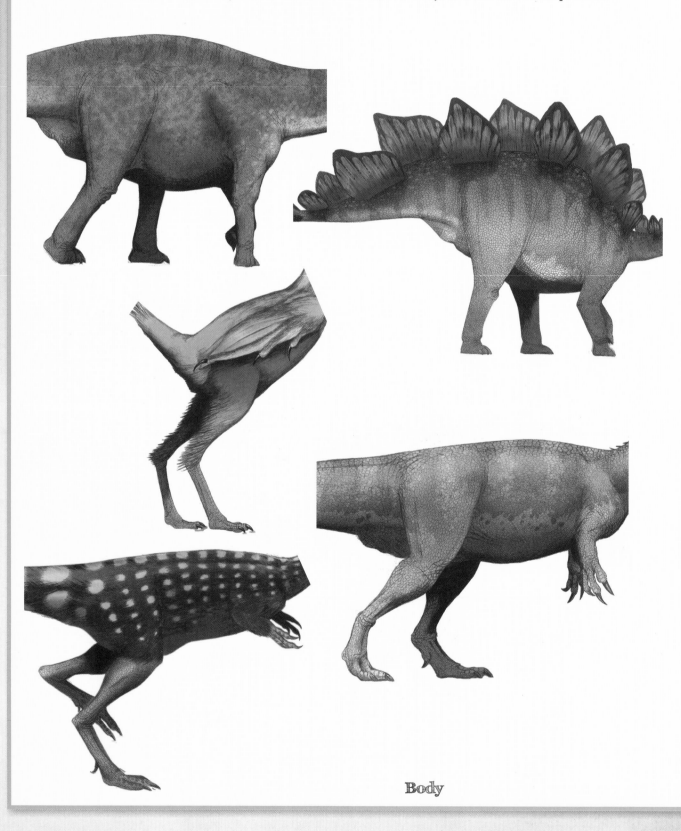

Body

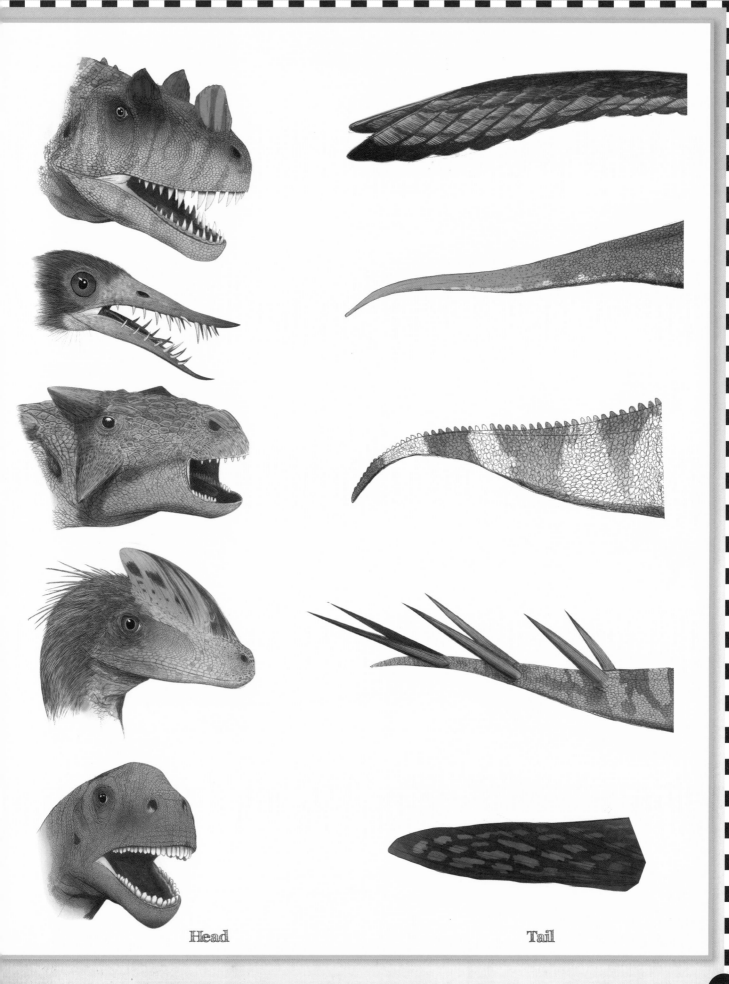

Head   Tail

25

Use these pages to create your own dinosaur species from the Late Jurassic!

Archaeopteryx lithographica

Location Observed: *Southern Germany*

Family: *Archaeopterygidae*

Length: *1.7 feet (0.5 meter)*

Height: *2.3 feet (0.7 meter) wingspan*

Weight: *1.1 pounds*

Temperament: *Cautious, curious*

Long, slim neck

Covered in dark feathers

Three-clawed wings

Did You Know?

Archaeopteryx was about the size of a modern hawk. But instead of being able to fly like a hawk, its clawed wings and feet allowed it to climb trees and then glide down on prey. It was also an adept runner.

First digit or "hallux" in opposing position

Killing claw on second digit

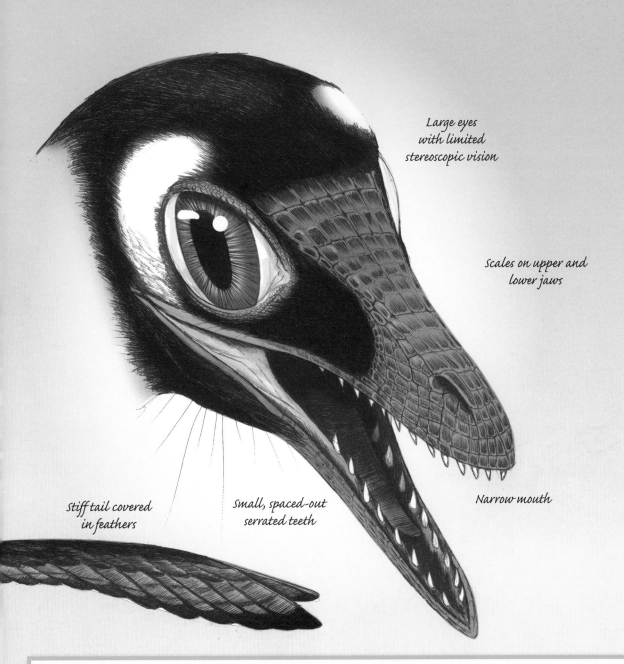

Large eyes
with limited
stereoscopic vision

Scales on upper and
lower jaws

Narrow mouth

Small, spaced-out
serrated teeth

Stiff tail covered
in feathers

Dino Decoding

Use the alphabet key on page 18 to decode these mystery words!

The Archaeopteryx is widely considered to be the _ _ _ _ _ _ _ _ _ _ _ between dinosaurs and modern birds.

$$\underline{}\ \underline{}\ \underline{}\ \underline{}\ \underline{}\ \underline{}\ \underline{}\quad \underline{}\ \underline{}\ \underline{}\ \underline{}$$

+ & / / & = ~   * & = (

ANSWER ON PAGE 156

Archaeopteryx Wing Detail

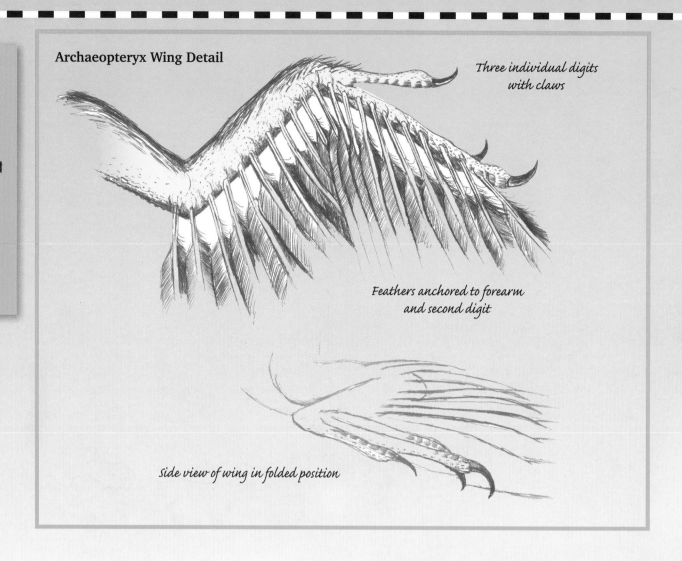

Three individual digits
with claws

Feathers anchored to forearm
and second digit

Side view of wing in folded position

Long feathers create
shape of tail

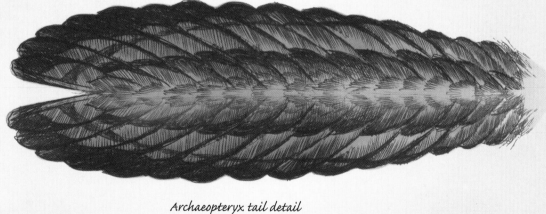

Archaeopteryx tail detail
(top view)

Two Archaeopteryx fighting over prey

Large, broad wings with black tips

Did You Know?

Archaeopteryx had limited flight capabilities. It spent most of its time in trees and on the ground.

Ceratosaurus nasicornis

Location Observed: *Colorado and Utah, United States*

Family: *Ceratosauridae*

Length: *20 feet (6 meters)*

Height: *7 feet (2 meters)*

Weight: *1,300 pounds*

Temperament: *Extremely aggressive*

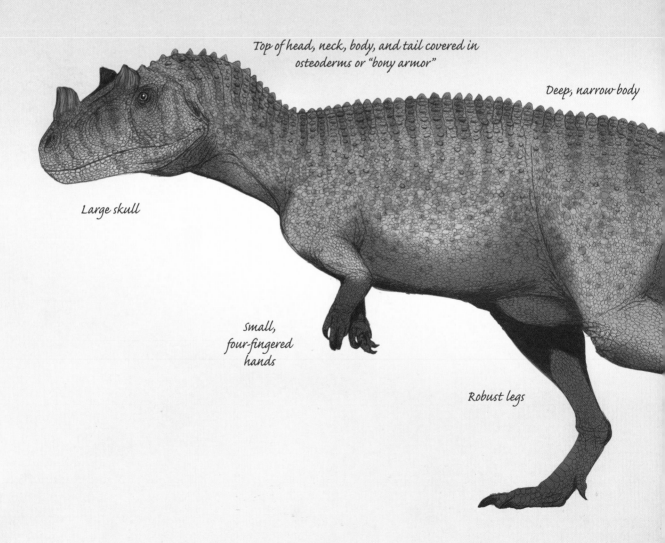

Top of head, neck, body, and tail covered in osteoderms or "bony armor"

Deep, narrow body

Large skull

Small, four-fingered hands

Robust legs

Three large horns used as mating display

Small eyes

Very large, flattened teeth

Lightly built jaw

Very deep and narrow tail

Did You Know?

Ceratosaurus means "horned lizard." At 20 feet long, Ceratosaurus was considered a medium-sized theropod.

Did You Know?

Although Ceratosaurus was capable of taking down large prey as well as scavenging for its meals, it hunted primarily by ambush.

Here Ceratosaurus attacks two unwary Dryosaurus

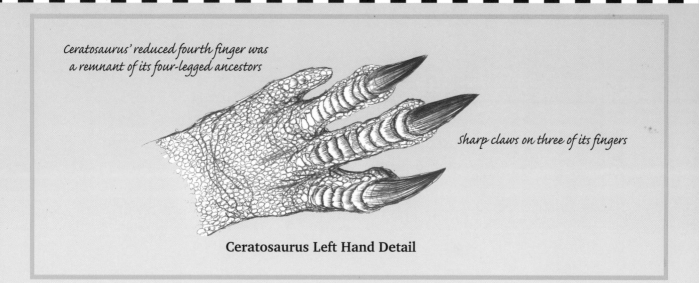

Ceratosaurus' reduced fourth finger was a remnant of its four-legged ancestors

sharp claws on three of its fingers

Ceratosaurus Left Hand Detail

Dryosaurus altus were 10-foot-long, plant-eating ornithischians with large hind limbs used for fleeing predators

True or False?

Most carnivorous dinosaurs had bony armor along their backs for protection.

ANSWER ON PAGE 156

Create a Volcano Scene

The Late Jurassic is known for heightened plate tectonic movement, which caused violent volcanoes and earthquakes as the land shifted. In fact, there's a volcano going off right here! Use stickers to fill the scene with dino spectators.

Compsognathus longipes

Location Observed: *Southern Germany and Southern France*

Family: *Compsognathidae*

Length: *4 feet (1.25 meters)*

Height: *1 foot (0.4 meter)*

Weight: *5.5 pounds*

Temperament: *shy, elusive*

Long, narrow build

Three-clawed forelimbs

Very long, thin legs designed
for speed

Relatively large feet

Did You Know?

At 4 feet long,
Compsognathus' torso
was only 1 foot of its
total length.

Large eyes placed at the sides of head

Two small crests at the base of snout

Long, slender snout

Long, flexible neck

Most of body covered in small proto-feathers

Long tail made up half of overall body length

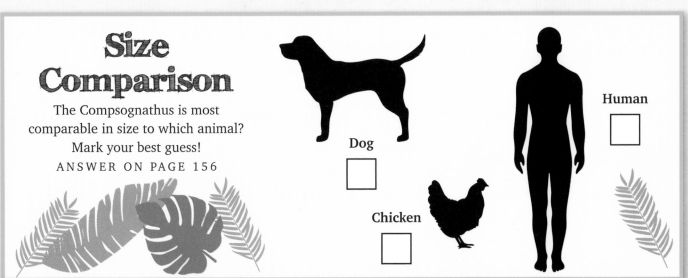

Size Comparison

The Compsognathus is most comparable in size to which animal? Mark your best guess!

ANSWER ON PAGE 156

Dog

Chicken

Human

Three-clawed hands with a larger thumb claw were used to both hunt and assist in eating small reptiles, fish, and insects

Compsognathus Hand Detail

Did You Know?

Compsognathus hunted along the shorelines of lagoons and small bodies of water.

Like birds, Compsognathus rested by lying down on its belly with its legs at its sides

Draw a Compsognathus

Using its small serrated teeth and flexible hands, Compsognathus quickly devours a small water snake. Draw this scene yourself! Use the blank grid below to copy what you see in each square at right. Start with a sketch, and then give it color with markers, colored pencils, or crayons!

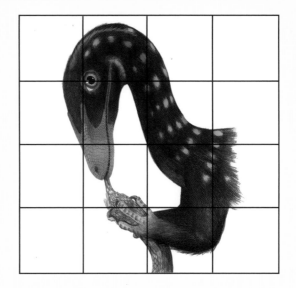

Guanlong wucaii

Location Observed: *Xinjiang, China*

Family: *Proceratosauridae*

Length: *11 feet (3.5 meters)*

Height: *5 feet (1.5 meters)*

Weight: *250 pounds*

Temperament: *Aggressive, territorial*

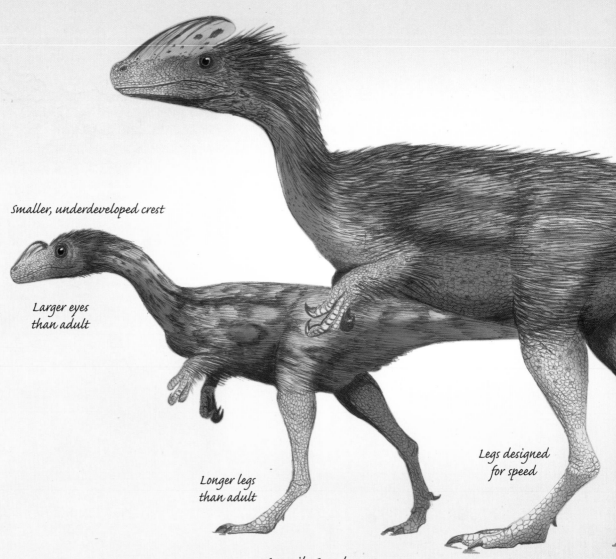

Smaller, underdeveloped crest

Larger eyes
than adult

Longer legs
than adult

Legs designed
for speed

Juvenile Guanlong
(approx. 6 years old)

Adult Guanlong

Covered in fibrous,
hair-like feathers

Large, bony crest
along the top of skull

Relatively long snout

Long, slim tail

Did You Know?

Guanlong is Chinese for
"crown dragon." At
11 feet long, Guanlong was
a formidable predator.

Spot the Differences

During mating season, fights break out as male Guanlongs battle for the affection of females. Can you spot the four differences between these two scenes?

ANSWERS ON PAGE 156

Word Scramble

The Guanlong is known for being the oldest relative of a famous dinosaur of the Cretaceous period. Can you unscramble the words below to reveal the dinosaur's name?

ANSWER ON PAGE 156

_ _ _ _ _ _ _ _ _ _ _ _ _ _ _ _ _ _ _

NYATRURNOAUSS EXR

Ornitholestes hermanni

Location Observed: Wyoming, United States

Family: Coeluridae

Length: 7 feet (2 meters)

Height: 2 feet (0.6 meter)

Weight: 30 pounds

Temperament: Aggressive

Long, thin neck

Body coated with long proto-feathers

Small head

Long, thin, flexible fingers

Long, slim legs

Did You Know?

Ornitholestes' body was about the size of a modern turkey.

Short, narrow head

Large eyes

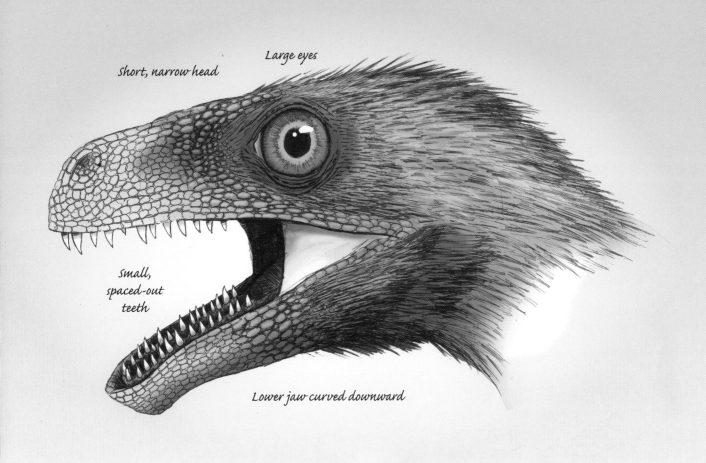

Small,
spaced-out
teeth

Lower jaw curved downward

Thin whip-like tail made up more
than half of total body length

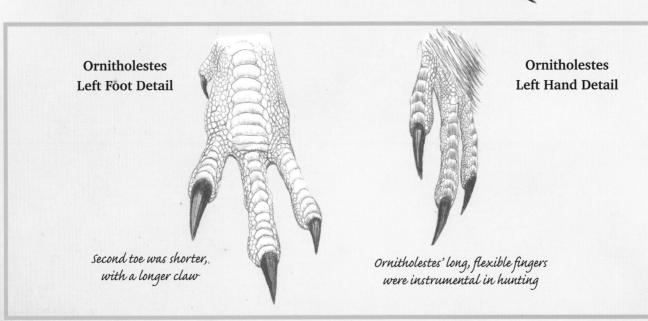

Ornitholestes
Left Foot Detail

Ornitholestes
Left Hand Detail

Second toe was shorter,
with a longer claw

Ornitholestes' long, flexible fingers
were instrumental in hunting

Ornitholestes used its speed to run down its prey. It fed mostly on lizards, young dinosaurs, fish, and small mammals.

Ornitholestes catches a Triconodon, an early mammal, and defends it from other predators

Tangle Maze

Ornitholestes may not be large, but it sure was speedy! Scientists estimate that it could run about 40 miles (64 kilometers) per hour!

Help this Ornitholestes reach its destination quickly. Which path should it take: A, B, or C?

ANSWER ON PAGE 156

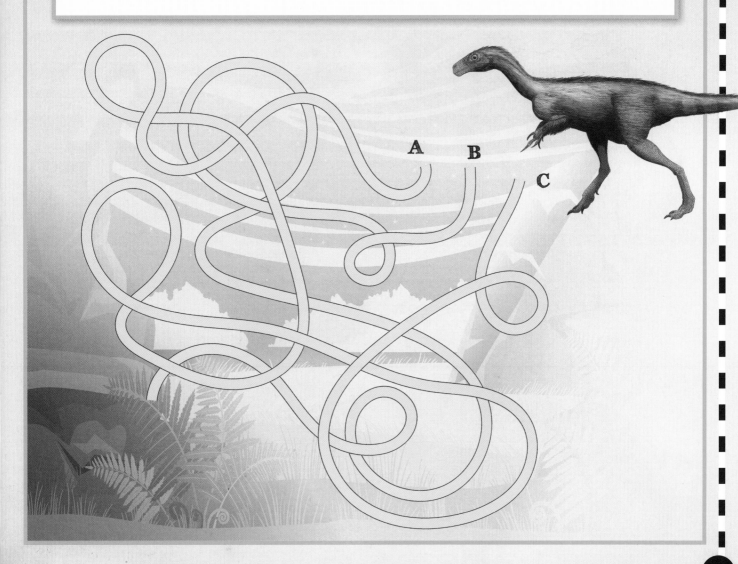

Torvosaurus tanneri

Location Observed: Colorado, Wyoming, and Utah, United States

Family: Megalosauridae

Length: 33 feet (10 meters)

Height: 9 feet (3 meters)

Weight: 2 tons

Temperament: Extremely aggressive

Dermal spines on head and neck

Long body

Large head

Powerful arms
with large
thumb claw

Short, muscular legs

Small eyes

Long, narrow head

Massive, long,
flat teeth

Powerful jaws

Did You Know?

With teeth reaching
5 inches (13 centimeters),
Torvosaurus was able to take
down prey much larger
than itself.

Thick, muscular neck used to pull large pieces of meat from prey

From the front, Torvosaurus presented a broad profile to intimidate other animals

Large feet

Dino Decoding

Use the alphabet key on page 18 to decode these mystery words! The Torvosaurus competed for prey alongside Allosaurus and Ceratosaurus. At the top of the food chain, Torvosaurus was an

@ | 5 1 | ? 5 $ @ 2 - ?

ANSWER ON PAGE 156

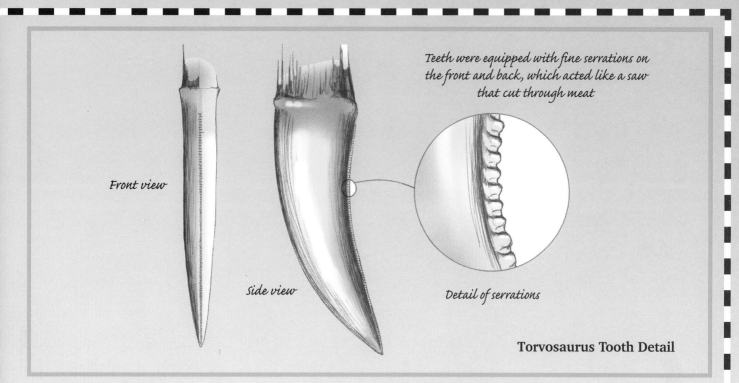

Teeth were equipped with fine serrations on the front and back, which acted like a saw that cut through meat

Front view

Side view

Detail of serrations

Torvosaurus Tooth Detail

Both a predator and scavenger, Torvosaurus' size allowed it to take over another dinosaur's meal

Yangchuanosaurus shangyouensis

Location Observed: *Yongchuan, China*

Family: *Metriacanthosauridae*

Length: *35 feet (11 meters)*

Height: *10 feet (3 meters)*

Weight: *3 tons*

Temperament: *Extremely aggressive*

Long, curved neck

Tall ridge along back

Deep, narrow torso

Strong arms with three gripping claws

Long legs designed for running

Did You Know?

Yangchuanosaurus was one of the largest predators in the Late Jurassic.

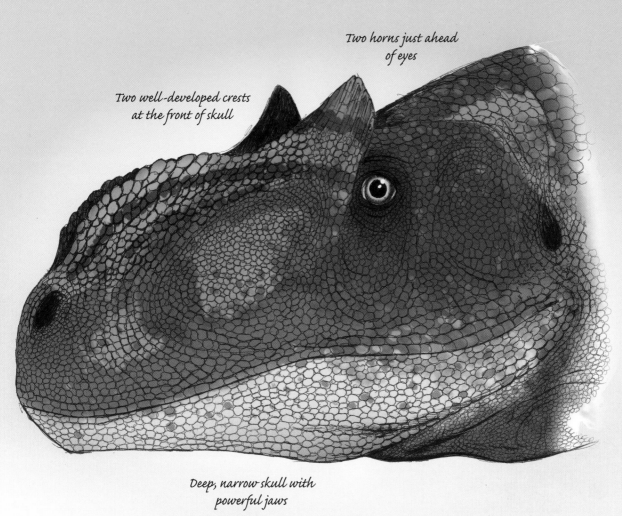

Two horns just ahead
of eyes

Two well-developed crests
at the front of skull

Deep, narrow skull with
powerful jaws

Long, deep tail

True or False

Read the three sentences below.
One is true and two are false.
Place a check mark next to the true statement!

☐ Yangchuanosaurus lived a solitary life and hunted alone.
☐ Yangchuanosaurus is closely related to Allosaurus.
☐ Yangchuanosaurus was a very slow runner.

ANSWER ON PAGE 156

Prehistoric Puzzle

Draw a line from each puzzle piece to where it belongs in the scene!

ANSWER ON PAGE 156

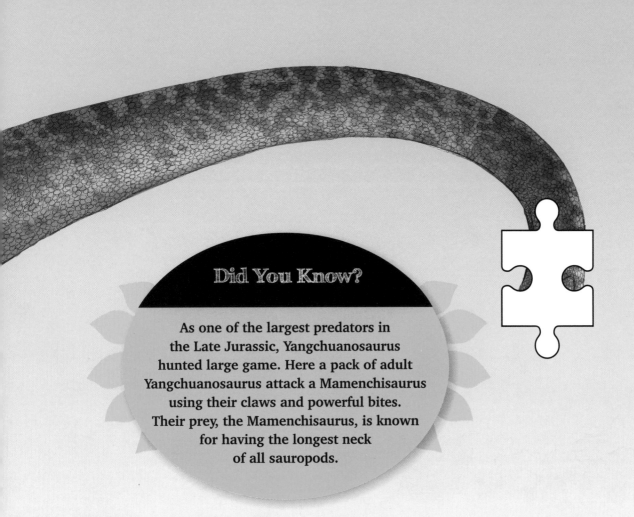

Did You Know?

As one of the largest predators in the Late Jurassic, Yangchuanosaurus hunted large game. Here a pack of adult Yangchuanosaurus attack a Mamenchisaurus using their claws and powerful bites. Their prey, the Mamenchisaurus, is known for having the longest neck of all sauropods.

Yi qi

Location Observed: *Hebei, China*

Family: *Scansoriopterygidae*

Length: *12 inches (0.3 meter)*

Height: *18 inches (0.45 meter) wingspan*

Weight: *0.84 pound*

Temperament: *Shy, elusive*

Short, blunt head

Slender neck

Body covered in
fibrous hair-like feathers

Large arms and
hands with
membrane
between fingers

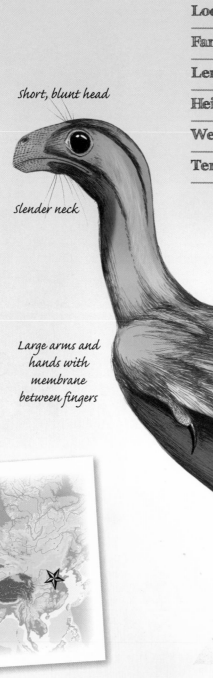

Long legs

Plumage on tail used as a display to attract mates

Large eyes placed on sides of head

Triangular-shaped head

Forward-facing teeth on front edge of jaws

Curved lower jaw

Did You Know?

At only 12 inches (0.3 meters) long, Yi qi is one of the smallest dinosaurs ever discovered.

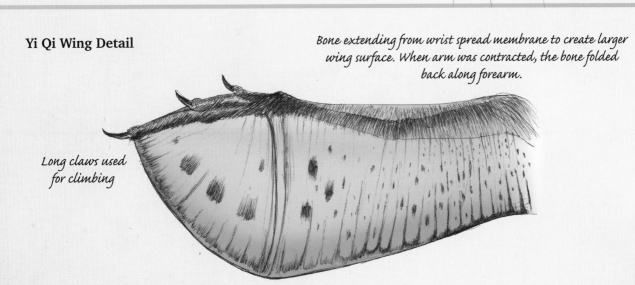

Yi Qi Wing Detail

Bone extending from wrist spread membrane to create larger wing surface. When arm was contracted, the bone folded back along forearm.

Long claws used for climbing

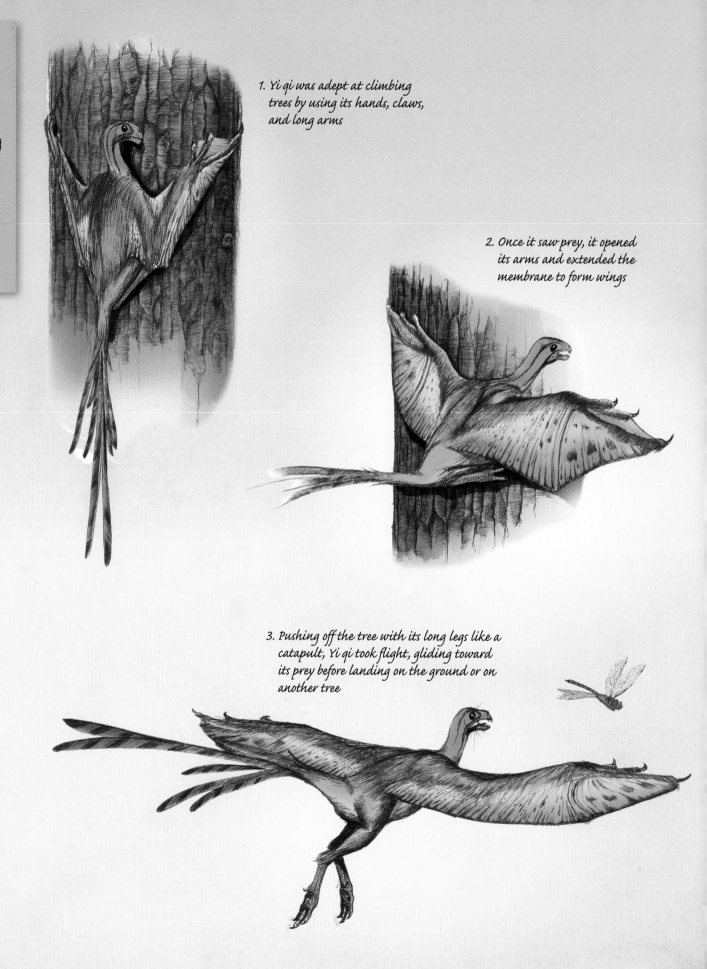

1. Yi qi was adept at climbing trees by using its hands, claws, and long arms

2. Once it saw prey, it opened its arms and extended the membrane to form wings

3. Pushing off the tree with its long legs like a catapult, Yi qi took flight, gliding toward its prey before landing on the ground or on another tree

Yi qi Path

In order to glide toward its prey, the Yi qi needs to start from a higher elevation.
Which path should it take to get to its meal?

ANSWER ON PAGE 157

Where in the World?

This map shows where these theropod fossils were discovered.
Place the dino sticker in the corresponding box!

ANSWERS ON PAGE 157

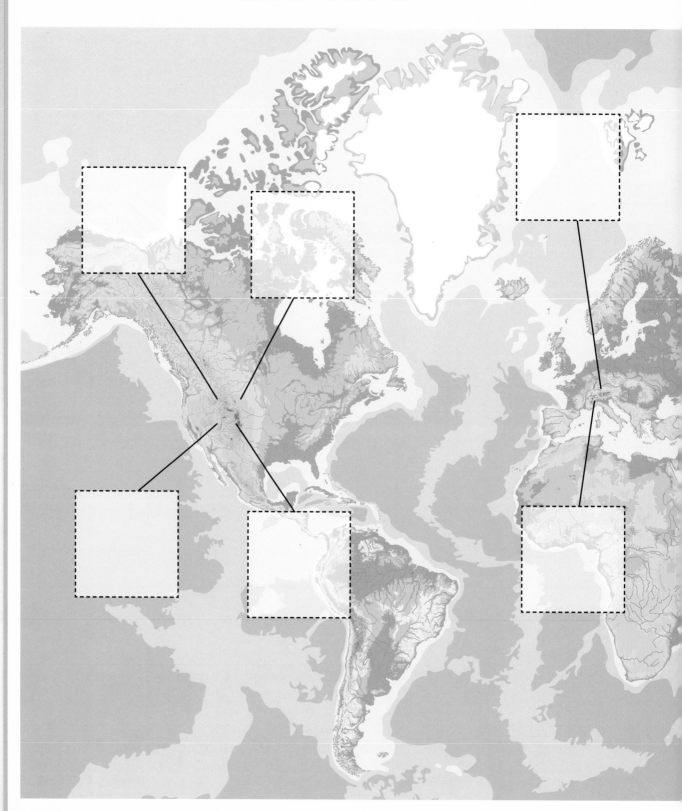

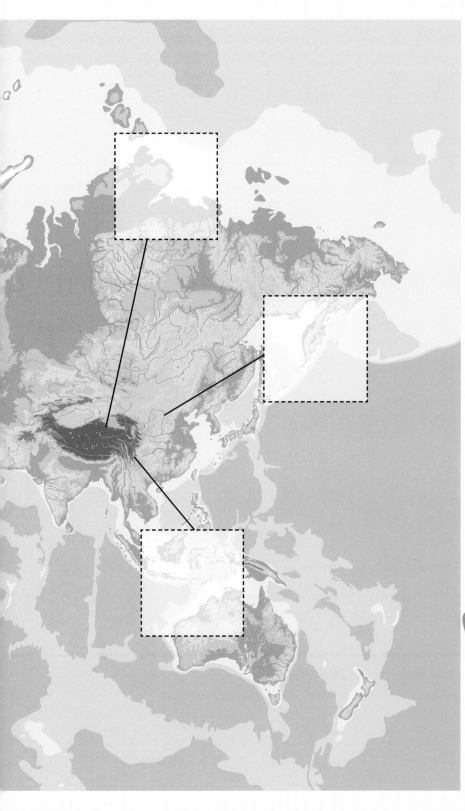

☐ **Allosaurus fragilis**

☐ **Archaeopteryx lithographica**

☐ **Ceratosaurus nasicornis**

☐ **Compsognathus longipes**

☐ **Guanlong wucaii**

☐ **Ornitholestes hermanni**

☐ **Torvosaurus tanneri**

☐ **Yangchuanosaurus shangyouensis**

☐ **Yi qi**

On the Offense

The theropods included some of the fiercest predators ever to walk the Earth. Here is a peek at some of the frightening characteristics that helped them track and attack their prey!

Good sense of smell

Powerful hind legs built for speed

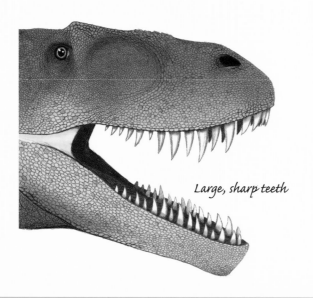

Large, sharp teeth

Long, sharp claws for grasping prey

Dino Diets

Fossils of teeth offer clues about what the dinosaurs ate. Sharp, serrated teeth belonged to meat-eaters who used them to tear through flesh and crush bone. In contrast, plant-eaters had either peg-like teeth used to strip leaves from branches or flat teeth used to grind plant matter.

Scientists also get diet clues from fossils of poop! They may appear to contain bone fragments or plant seeds, helping scientists determine the dinosaur's diet. Want to know the name for fossilized droppings? Use the alphabet key on page 18 to decode the answer below!

ANSWER ON PAGE 157

9 - | ? - * & 2 5

What Am I?

Test your detective instincts as you figure out each theropod below.
Find and place the matching stickers!

ANSWERS ON PAGE 157

Dino 1

My narrow mouth has small, serrated teeth, and my neck is long. I have feathers and wings that allow me to glide down toward my prey. I'm pretty fast on my feet too! What am I?

> Place sticker here

Dino 2

Stay far away from me! I am an apex predator with powerful jaws, massive teeth, small eyes, and spines on the top of my head. My fossils have been found in North America. What am I?

> Place sticker here

Dino 3

I'm about the size of a turkey, but I'm still a great hunter! I can even run about 40 miles (64 kilometers) per hour. This helps me catch my meals, which include small mammals, fish, and even young dinosaurs. What am I?

> Place sticker here

Dino 4

My head, neck, body, and tail are covered in bony armor called osteoderms. I have sharp claws on three of my fingers, but the fourth is a short remnant of my four-legged ancestors. My name means "horned lizard." What am I?

> Place sticker here

Dino 5

My body is covered in hair-like feathers, and my long tail plumage is used to attract mates. I'm good at climbing trees, and I extend the membrane on my wings to glide toward my prey. What am I?

> Place sticker here

Sauropods

Our journey continues deep into the Late Jurassic to explore the largest land animals ever: the sauropods. Spread before you are vast forests of early pine trees reaching as high as 100 feet above the ground. At your feet are beds of thick green ferns and cycad plants covering the ground like an endless carpet, with intermittent dark tree trunks breaking up the green color. Pterosaurs glide through the air, effortlessly picking up insects without ever breaking their rhythm. It is generally silent with the occasional squawk of a pterosaur and the snap of branches from the trees above. As you look up, a thick neck extends upward, ending in an almost imperceptible head. It forcefully pulls back, breaking another branch. At the base of the neck is a colossal body held up by four pillar-like legs. This animal is so big, it cannot be seen all at once.

It quietly goes about its business as another much heavier and longer animal joins in, turning its attention to the lower plants. It strips the leaves from entire fern plants systematically with its mouth, one at a time, moving its neck from plant to plant while keeping its body still. Others begin to appear through the trees, each oblivious to one another as they continue to feed. You are in the unmistakable company of sauropods.

Sauropods were by far the heaviest and longest land animals to ever exist. They were known for their large, elephant-like bodies with long necks and tails. Though most were gigantic, some species only reached the size of a large bull.

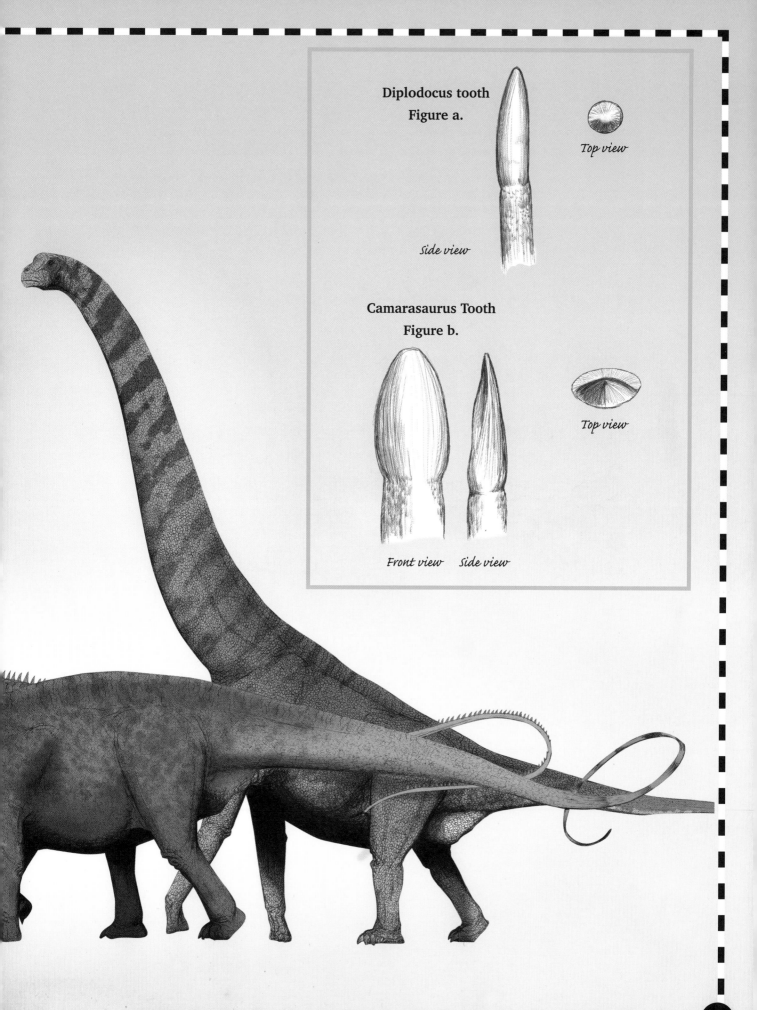

Diplodocus tooth
Figure a.

Top view

Side view

Camarasaurus Tooth
Figure b.

Top view

Front view   *Side view*

Regardless of their size, all were designed to be efficient eaters. Some consumed hundreds of pounds of plant matter daily in order to maintain their mass. Sauropod heads were typically small with teeth lining the front edges of their jaws. They did not chew or crush plants with their mouths, but rather swallowed them whole.

Their teeth were specialized for two different eating techniques: stripping or tearing. Peg-like teeth (fig. a) were for stripping the leaves from a plant; chiseled teeth (fig. b) were for tearing and cutting leaves and branches. Teeth were shed and replaced as needed every few days to every few months as they wore down.

Sauropods' large, bloated trunks contained fermentation chambers called "caecum," which processed raw plant matter and extracted nutrients starting at the gizzard and continuing all the way through the intestines. Their necks were also instrumental in eating. Most species evolved long necks for either reaching higher-growing plants or covering a large area of low-lying plants without having to move their bodies.

Sauropods hatched from eggs and were born precocial, meaning they were fully capable of feeding and walking without assistance from their parents. Nests were usually communal, consisting of many individuals laying eggs in one area. Like modern sea turtles, only a small percentage of sauropod hatchlings survived predation and made it into adulthood. Of the surviving few, juveniles formed groups and eventually herds, seeking safety in numbers.

Did You Know?

To counterbalance their heavy necks and torsos, sauropods evolved heavy tails. These tails became specialized as well, some becoming defensive weapons with long whips or hammer-like clubs.

A newborn Brachiosaurus hatchling makes its way out of its egg and joins others seeking safety

Sauropods of the Late Jurassic

The Late Jurassic is known as "the era of giants." Sauropods evolved and flourished into species more gigantic than the Earth has ever or will ever see again. It is during this period that some of the most recognizable dinosaurs, like the Brontosaurus and Diplodocus, live. The Late Jurassic landscape is abundant with herds of great sauropods moving in a constant search for food.

This section explores three basic families of sauropods. First is the Diplodocidae, known for their long horizontal bodies, teeth at the front of their mouths, and long whipping tails which made up about half of their overall body length. This group includes species like *Brontosaurus louisae* and *Diplodocus hallorum*. Second is the Camarasauridae family, with relatively short upright necks and larger heads, with the nasal opening in their skull ahead of their eyes. This family is represented by its namesake *Camarasaurus supremus*. And finally, the Brachiosauridae family is best known for their giraffe-like posture, with their forelimbs longer than their hind limbs, causing them to carry their necks vertically. This family is represented by one of the best-studied species: *Giraffatitan brancai*.

In the following pages, explore these magnificent animals in detail and see their specialized adaptations for both eating and survival.

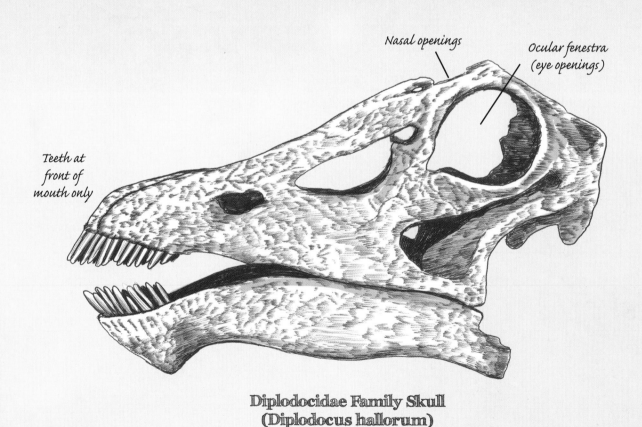

Nasal openings

Ocular fenestra
(eye openings)

Teeth at
front of
mouth only

**Diplodocidae Family Skull
(Diplodocus hallorum)**

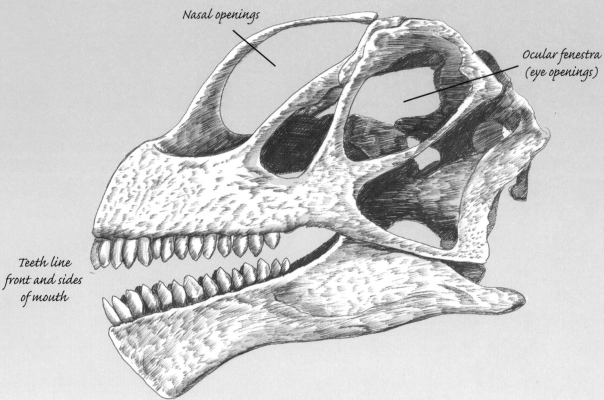

Nasal openings

Ocular fenestra
(eye openings)

Teeth line
front and sides
of mouth

**Camarasauridae Family Skull
(Camarasaurus supremus)**

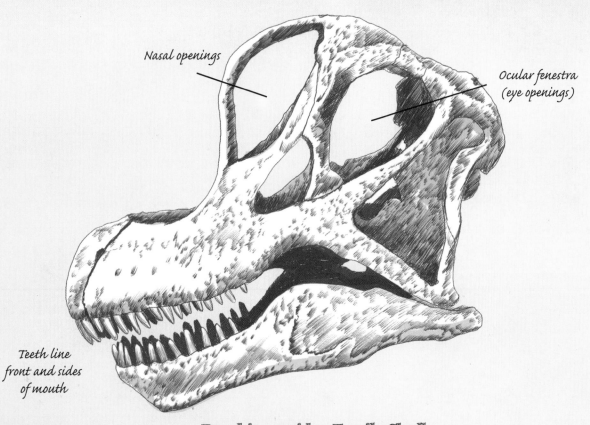

Nasal openings

Ocular fenestra
(eye openings)

Teeth line
front and sides
of mouth

**Brachiosauridae Family Skull
(Giraffatitan brancai)**

Spot the Difference

Sauropods often traveled in herds for protection. On this page, one of these dinos is not like the others! Can you spot it?

ANSWER ON PAGE 157

Sauropod Word Search

As you continue to learn about sauropods, remember these important words!
They are also buried in the word search below. Can you find them all?

ANSWERS ON PAGE 157

- ☐ Brachiosauridae
- ☐ Caecum
- ☐ Camarasauridae
- ☐ Diplodocidae
- ☐ The era of giants
- ☐ Heavy tails
- ☐ Long neck
- ☐ Plant eater
- ☐ Precocial
- ☐ Quadropedal

```
P H G U M V L T M Y A A O C V W P B K Z
C L E Y L E H H G G L N Z Q N U R R H N
T T I A L R D K G V P N L U J J E A L E
P K H Y V J T L K X R F Q A V Q C C L X
C X T E Y Y B R S S H I U D T M O H G F
N A H W E Q T N H U R M K R A R C I U K
R G M P B R R A C T D K C O T U I O M T
D G N A K D A O I B O D W P J C A S E W
Q W O R R Y Z O X L R C O E S D L A V P
V N A N J A K L F R S F T D O E I U C O
G R A C T D S K V G Y E Z A M H J R G W
Y D P N E L Q A N J I L L L N J S I Q Y
J N E P J M E C U L W A Y S B Z F D K K
B K L B O T X D G R W R N F L C U A C F
Y O W S N E Y L M K I Y D T F A P E A X
E M T F O U H N L G M D K P S E A J S D
D I P L O D O C I D A E A N S C Z R O J
S Q Y C U V T Z R D V E I E U U Z K I Q
P H U L W G Y O O W P R B L J M W M R Z
L O N G N E C K G P L A N T E A T E R A
```

Sauropod Maze Craze

Help the Brontosaurus make its way through the maze to its breakfast!

ANSWER ON PAGE 157

Test Your Memory

Can you put these geologic periods in order? Use numbers 1 through 4 to fill in the blanks. Hint! See pages 6-7.

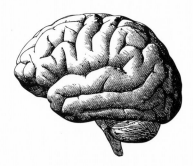

- ☐ **Jurassic Period**
- ☐ **Permian Period**
- ☐ **Cretaceous Period**
- ☐ **Triassic Period**

ANSWERS ON PAGE 157

Guess Who?

Guess the dinosaur's diet! Write "meat-eater" or "plant-eater" in the blank beneath each tooth.

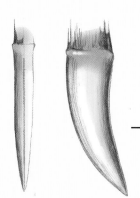

_____

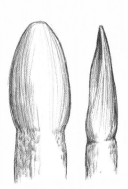

_____

Do these belong to a sauropod or a therapod?

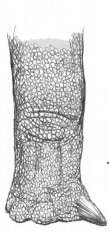

_____

_____

ANSWERS ON PAGE 157

Brontosaurus louisae

Long, rectangular head

Long, thick, and deep neck

Tall ridge along back

Small eyes

Short forelimbs

Long jaw

Narrow, blunt teeth for stripping leaves off plants

Location Observed: *Utah, United States*

Family: *Diplodocidae*

Length: *75 feet (23 meters)*

Height: *17 feet (5.2 meters)*

Weight: *20 tons*

Temperament: *Defensive, aggressive*

Long tail with whip-like end

Dino Decoding

What does the word "Brontosaurus" mean in Greek?

ANSWER ON PAGE 158

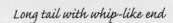

2	^	>	=	$	5	?		*	&	#	@	?	$

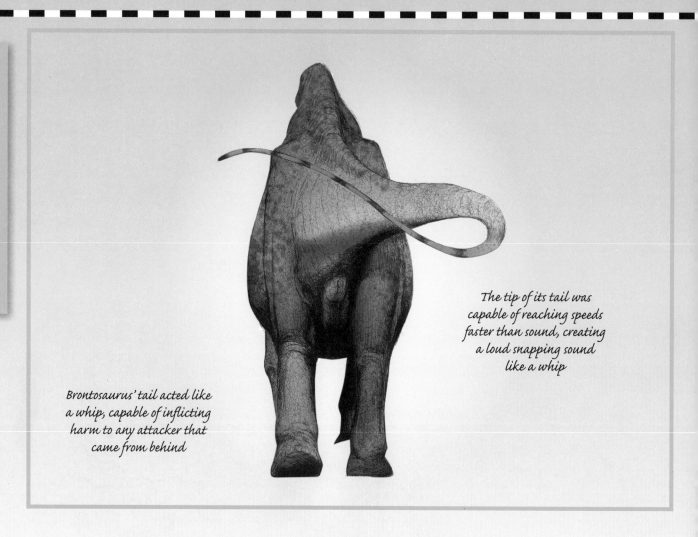

The tip of its tail was capable of reaching speeds faster than sound, creating a loud snapping sound like a whip

Brontosaurus' tail acted like a whip, capable of inflicting harm to any attacker that came from behind

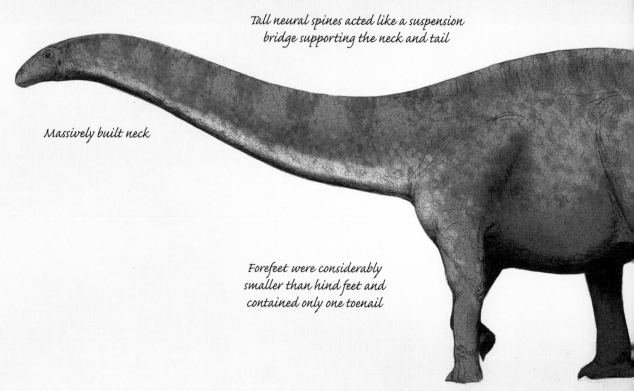

Tall neural spines acted like a suspension bridge supporting the neck and tail

Massively built neck

Forefeet were considerably smaller than hind feet and contained only one toenail

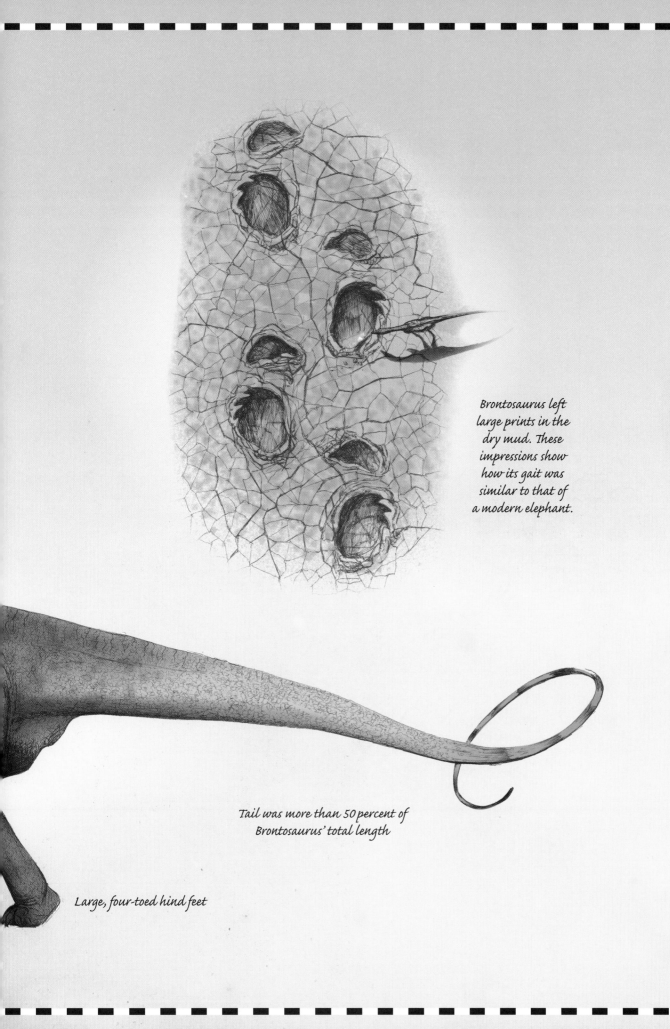

Brontosaurus left large prints in the dry mud. These impressions show how its gait was similar to that of a modern elephant.

Tail was more than 50 percent of Brontosaurus' total length

Large, four-toed hind feet

Short, blunt head

Large head for
a sauropod

Relatively thick,
short neck

Tall shoulders

Did You Know?

Compared to most of the
giant sauropods of the Late
Jurassic, *Camarasaurus
supremus* is considered
medium-sized.

Forelimbs shorter
than hind limbs

Single-toed
forefeet

Four-toed
hind feet

Camarasaurus supremus

Location Observed: *Colorado, Wyoming, and Utah, United States*

Family: *Camarasauridae*

Length: *50 feet (15 meters)*

Height: *17 feet (5.2 meters)*

Weight: *15 tons*

Temperament: *Social, cautious*

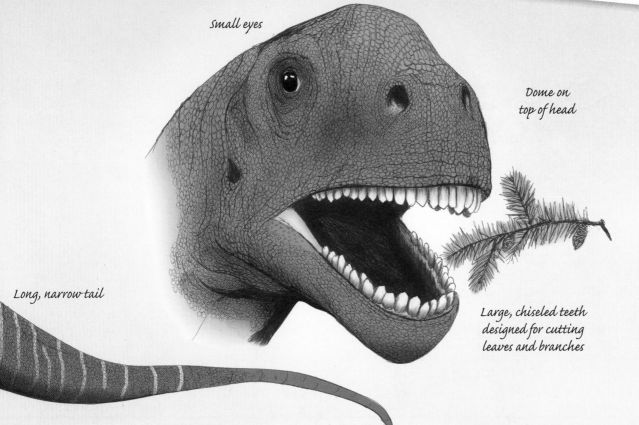

Small eyes

Dome on top of head

Large, chiseled teeth designed for cutting leaves and branches

Long, narrow tail

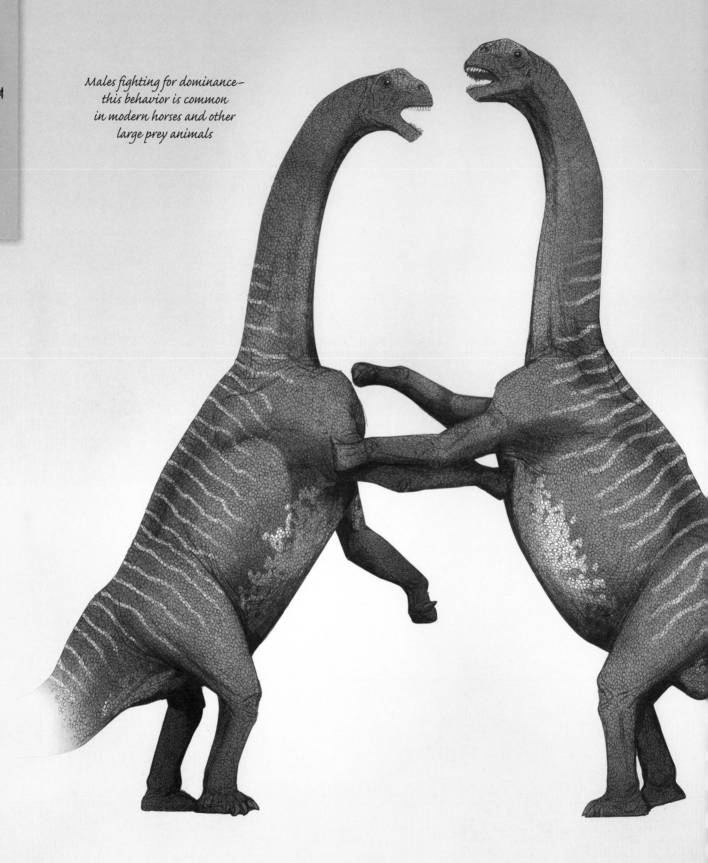

Males fighting for dominance—
this behavior is common
in modern horses and other
large prey animals

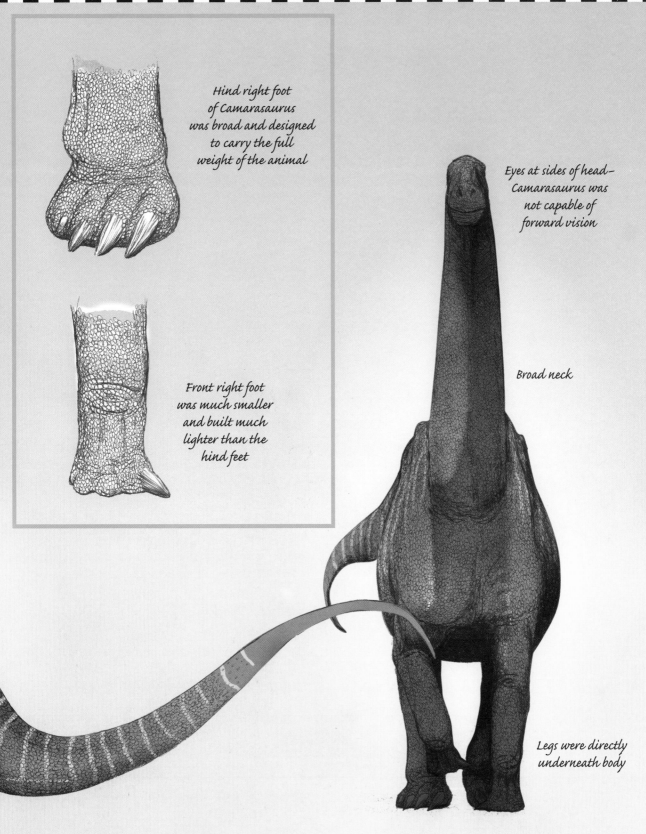

Hind right foot of Camarasaurus was broad and designed to carry the full weight of the animal

Front right foot was much smaller and built much lighter than the hind feet

Eyes at sides of head— Camarasaurus was not capable of forward vision

Broad neck

Legs were directly underneath body

Front View of Camarasaurus

Create a Scene

Use stickers to bring this Jurassic scene to life!

High ridge along back and base of tail

Dermal spines running from head to tail

Very long tail ending in a whip-like tip

Powerfully built hind limbs

Thinner, shorter forelimbs

Diplodocus hallorum

Location Observed: *Colorado and Utah, United States*

Family: *Diplodocidae*

Length: *80 feet (25 meters)*

Height: *20 feet (6 meters)*

Weight: *12 tons*

Temperament: *Social, cautious*

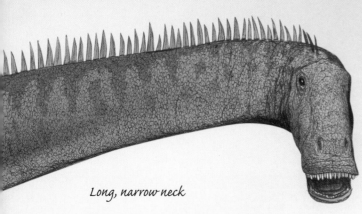

Long, narrow neck

Flat and wide mouth

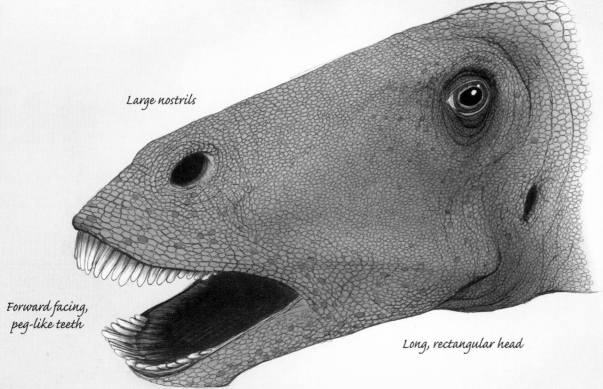

Large nostrils

Forward facing,
peg-like teeth

Long, rectangular head

Did You Know?

Using its 40-foot-long muscular tail as a defensive weapon, Diplodocus whipped back and forth, preventing any attacker from getting close.

Small head compared to body size

Narrow, lightly built body

Tall, thin limbs hold the body high off the ground

One lash from Diplodocus' tail
could kill or seriously injure
a theropod

Tail was more than 50 percent
of overall body length

Thin, tapered portion of tail
made up almost half the
tail's length

Giraffatitan brancai

Location Observed: *Tanzania, Africa*

Family: *Brachiosauridae*

Length: *75 feet (23 meters)*

Height: *50 feet (15 meters)*

Weight: *40 tons*

Temperament: *Defensive, aggressive*

Did You Know?

For many years, *Giraffatitan brancai* was known as *Brachiosaurus brancai*.

Back slopes upward

Tail much shorter
than neck

Short hind limbs

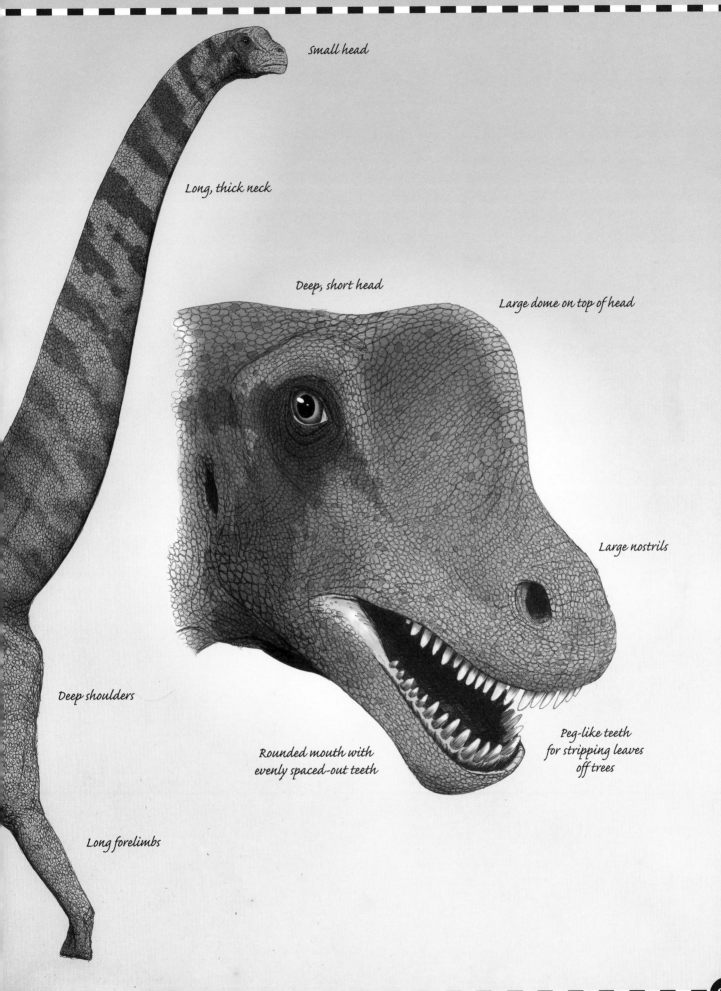

Small head

Long, thick neck

Deep, short head

Large dome on top of head

Large nostrils

Deep shoulders

Peg-like teeth
for stripping leaves
off trees

Rounded mouth with
evenly spaced-out teeth

Long forelimbs

Did You Know?

Herds of Giraffatitan traveled together, seeking protection in numbers. Most individuals were juveniles weighing 1 ton or more.

In the shadow of a giant – a 40-ton adult Giraffatitan dwarfs the smaller juveniles

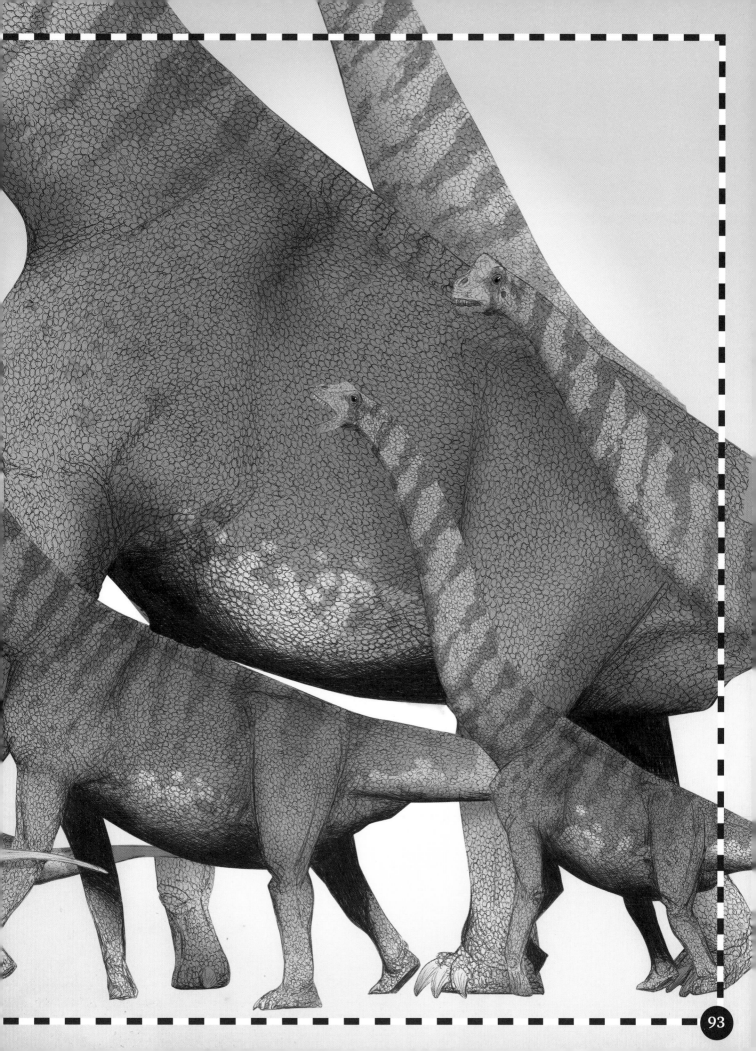

A Prehistoric Trip to Remember

Create a random list of words using the prompts below.
Then fill in the corresponding words to complete your story. Remember that a noun is a person, place, or thing. An adjective is a descriptive word, and a verb is an action. Try not to laugh!

Plural Noun: _____   Verb: _____

Adjective: _____   Adjective: _____

Number: _____   Noun: _____

Adjective: _____   Number: _____

Adjective: _____   Verb: _____

Plural Noun: _____   Adjective: _____

Plural Noun: _____

Calling all dinosaur lovers, paleontologists, and _____: Now is your chance
        Plural Noun

to hop aboard our _____ time machine and travel back to the Late Jurassic!
   Adjective

It's a balmy _____ degrees with green, _____ vegetation as far as the eye can
    Number   *Adjective*

see. You may encounter a herd of _____ sauropods feeding on _____ or a
             Adjective   *Plural Noun*

theropod with long, sharp _____ chasing its prey. At twilight, it's a real treat
           Plural Noun

to watch the pterosaurs _____ across the sky. You can even bring home a small
      Verb

souvenir, such as a _____ leaf or a _____. Just don't miss the trip home or
     Adjective   *Noun*

you'll be stuck in the Jurassic for _____ years. Are you ready for the adventure
        Number

of a lifetime? Don't delay—_____ onto the time machine and we'll give you a
     Verb

_____ good time!
Adjective

Ancient Art

Use colored pencils, crayons, or markers to bring this Diplodocus to life!

Number Maze

Help the Allosaurus catch the Camarasaurus! Work your way through the maze in order from 1 to 21. You can move up, down, left, or right!

1	2	78	28	80	48	98
79	3	4	5	6	58	90
1	4	3	27	7	29	30

31	32	33	34	5	6	7	8	39	40
41	42	43	44	45	46	47	9	49	50
88	26	53	14	13	12	11	10	59	60
61	62	63	15	14	66	67	68	69	70
74	72	73	16	15	18	77			
81	82	83	17	16	19	20			
91	64	93	18	19	20	21			

ANSWER ON PAGE 158

Where in the World?

This map shows where these sauropod fossils have been found.
Place the dino sticker in the corresponding box!

ANSWERS ON PAGE 158

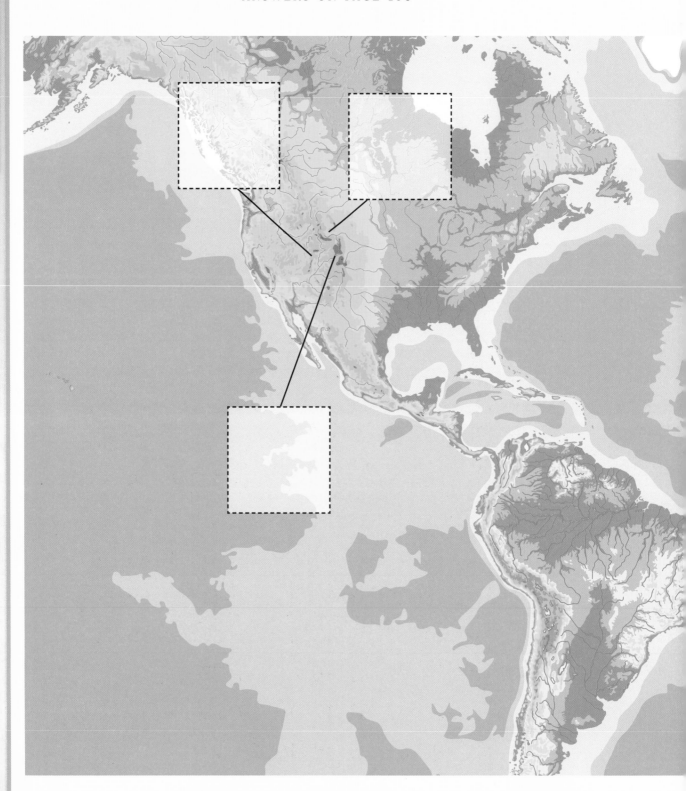

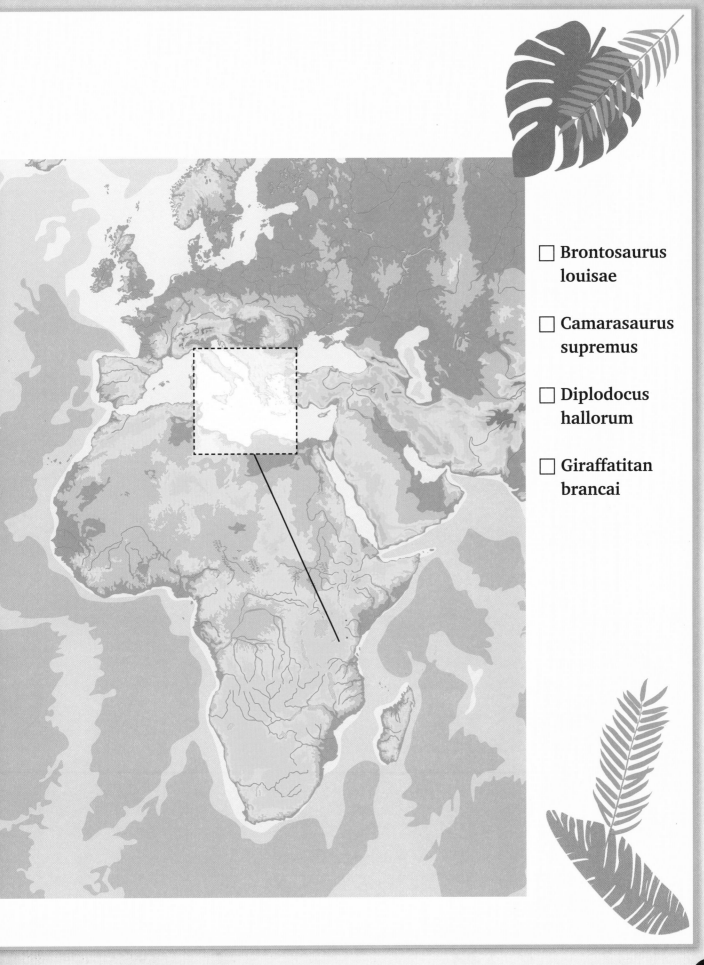

- ☐ Brontosaurus louisae
- ☐ Camarasaurus supremus
- ☐ Diplodocus hallorum
- ☐ Giraffatitan brancai

Ornithischians

It's a foggy morning as the Jurassic sun begins to rise over a field of horsetail plants. As you walk into a field, trees slowly begin to appear through the fog, making themselves more visible with each step you take. There is a drone of insects and mosquitoes in your ear, punctuated by the low grunts and snorting sounds coming from a nearby large animal. The air is thick with humidity and the odor of dung, reminiscent of a farm or petting zoo. The grunting noises continue just ahead of you, as a towering object begins to take shape through the fog. The object moves away from you as it slowly reveals itself—it's an immense dinosaur feeding on the plants beneath it. A cloud of insects forms around its nose and lands on its nostrils. With another deep snort from the dinosaur, the insects disband before reassembling. Its head moves downward as it takes in a mouthful of horsetail plants. Using its hardened beak, it cuts the plants cleanly, then crushes them with its teeth and swallows.

It is now in plain sight. The unmistakable plates on its back tell you it's a Stegosaurus and it's massive—over 12 feet tall and 20 feet long, about the size of a modern-day elephant. As you approach to get a closer look, the Stegosaurus becomes agitated and begins to rear up as if to say "stay away." This behavior is no different than approaching any wild animal that feels threatened. The fog has now almost entirely lifted, and more animals in the field are now visible. You realize that you are standing among dozens of dinosaurs, all grazing on the same pasture of plants. Many species of ornithischian dinosaurs have come together to peacefully feed, as they have many times in the past. This is a typical breakfast in the Late Jurassic.

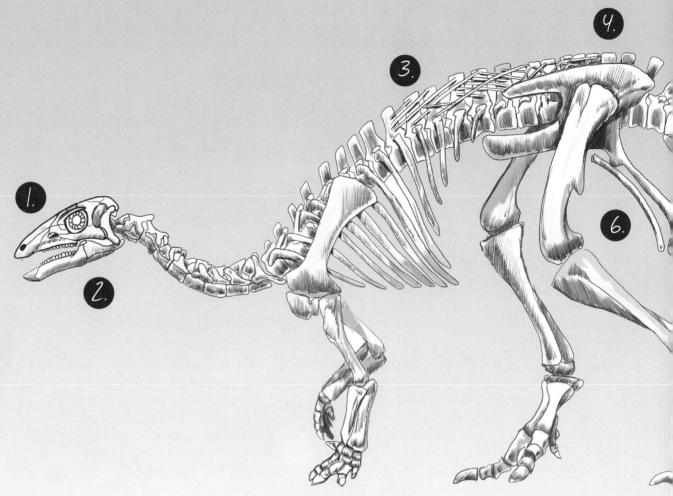

1.
2.
3.
4.
6.

Camptosaurus Dispar Skeleton

Ornithischians were one of the two major orders of dinosaurs, the other being saurischian (which includes theropods and sauropods). They were known for their hip structure, beaked mouths, and for being herbivores or "plant-eaters." Ornithischians were an extremely diverse group, including many different body types and self-defense methods. Even their means of locomotion was diverse: some were bipedal (walking on two legs), others were quadrupedal (walking on four legs), while many were capable of switching between both. If you compare ornithischians to modern-day animals, they would be considered large prey animals, such as horses, cattle, rhinoceroses, and even elephants, as they all had very different body types and means of self-defense, and yet were all herbivorous. Some of the more famous ornithischian dinosaurs include Stegosaurus, Triceratops (Late Cretaceous), Ankylosaurus (Cretaceous), and Hadrosaurs or "duck-billed dinosaurs" (Late Cretaceous).

What Makes an Ornithischian?

1. bony beak at front of skull
2. teeth for grinding plant matter
3. bony tendons crisscrossing vertebrae
4. ilium bone is narrow
5. ischium bone faces back
6. pubis bone faces back

Ornithischians of the Late Jurassic

By the Late Jurassic, most ornithischians had clearly developed means by which to confront or escape predators—none more evident than the *Stegosaurus stenops* and *Kentrosaurus aethiopicus*. Both dinosaurs had tails clad with sharp, spiked horns and plates rising from their backs. With this deterrent, few, if any, predators were willing to challenge a healthy adult. Kentrosaurus even had 3-foot-long spikes protruding from its shoulders to avoid ambush from the sides. Others like *Gargoyleosaurus parkpinorum* preferred a passive form of self-defense. Built wide, low to the ground, and armored literally from the nose to the tip of its tail, Gargoyleosaurus made itself a difficult meal to be had. This dinosaur was the ancestor of future dinosaurs from the Cretaceous, like Ankylosaurus, which developed more active forms of self-defense by using a bony growth on the tip of its tail as a club to ward off attackers. Other species like *Camptosaurus dispar* evolved with larger hind limbs and smaller forelimbs. Because of this, it could outrun many of its predators. When given no means of escape, Camptosaurus was also equipped with a large thumb claw used as a formidable weapon.

Explore the ornithischian dinosaurs in the following pages, and see how they survived the dangers of the Late Jurassic.

On the Defense

The ornithischians may have been herbivores, but they were still well-equipped with formidable weapons. After all, they needed to protect themselves against some of the fiercest predators ever to walk the Earth. Male ornithischians also competed with each other for dominance. Here is a peek at some of the ways ornithischians were great warriors!

Fused, armor-like scales

Horns

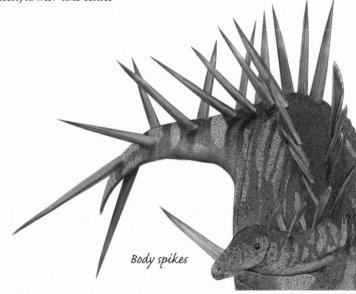

Body spikes

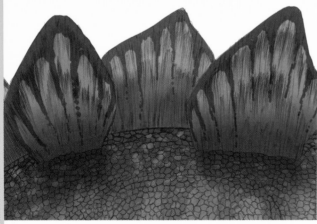

Plates

Thumb spikes

Jurassic Crossing

Dinosaurs were the largest group of animals to walk the Earth. And you've already learned about so many! Answer the questions below and fill in the puzzle.

ANSWERS ON PAGE 158

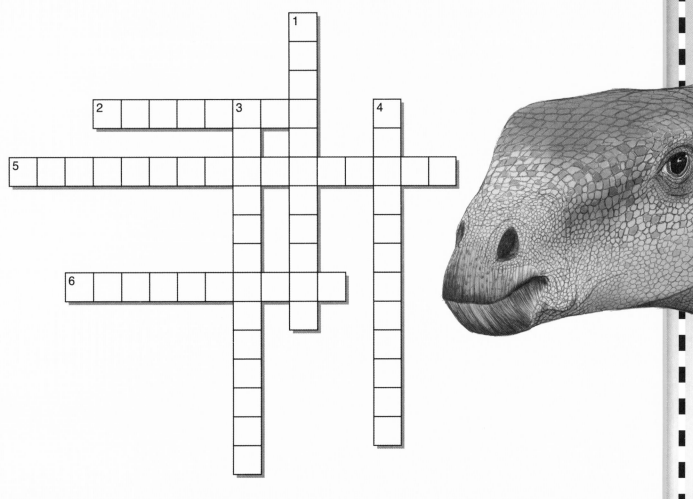

Across:

2. I have a long snout and a large, bony crest along my skull. My name is Chinese for "crown dragon." I am a _____.

5. I was one of the largest predators in the Late Jurassic. I had two horns just ahead of my eyes, and two well-developed crests at the front of my skull. I am an _____.

6. I had dermal spines running from my head to my tail. I am extremely long, with a whip-like tail, but I'm built lighter than most other sauropods. I am a _____.

Down:

1. I am an ornithischian with an alternating row of armor plates along my back and tail. I am much larger than my cousin, Kentrosaurus. I am a _____.

3. I ran on two legs and was very fast to catch my prey. My body was covered in proto-feathers, and I was about the size of a modern turkey. I am an _____.

4. I have a large dome on top of my head, and I travel in large herds. I have a long, thick neck and peg-like teeth for stripping leaves off trees. I am a _____.

Camptosaurus dispar

Location Observed: Wyoming, United States

Family: Camptosauridae

Length: 16 feet (5 meters)

Height: 6 feet (1.8 meters)

Weight: 1,000 pounds

Temperament: Reclusive, shy

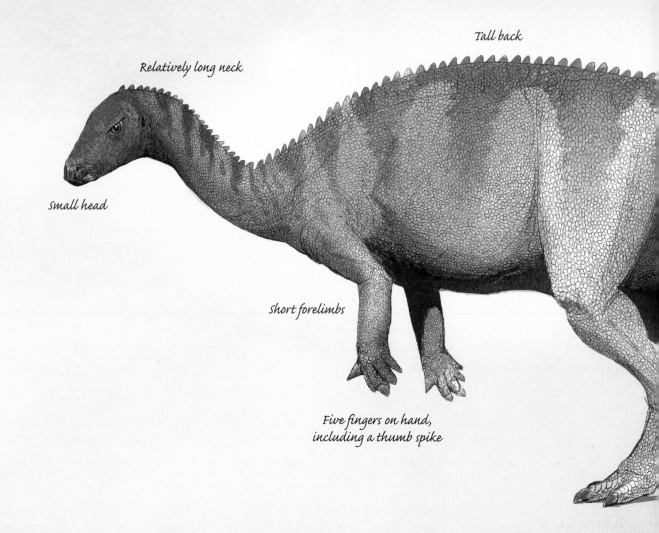

Tall back

Relatively long neck

Small head

Short forelimbs

Five fingers on hand,
including a thumb spike

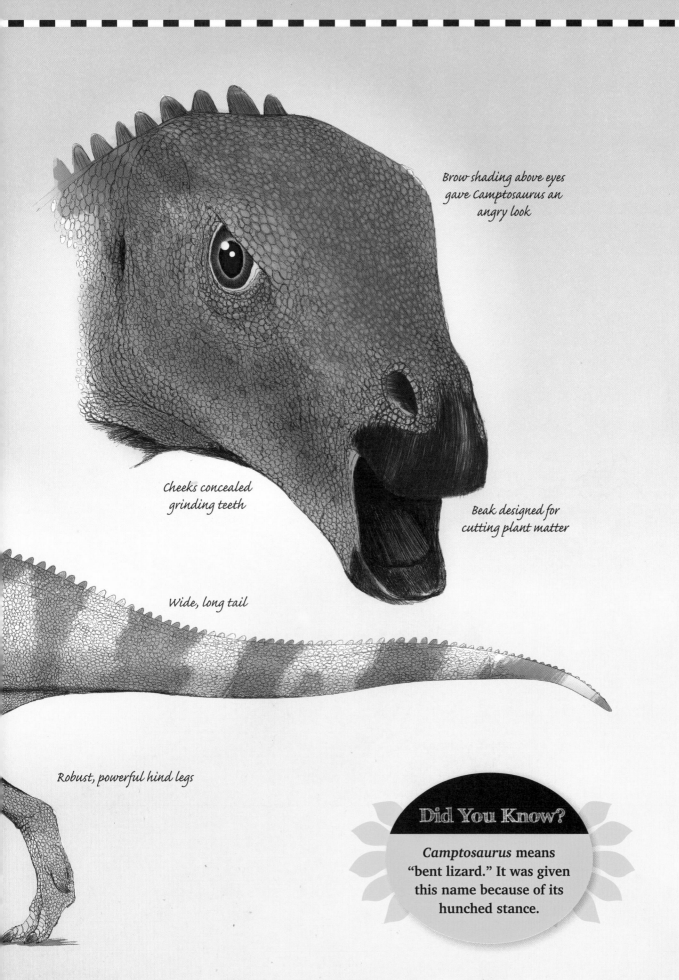

Brow shading above eyes gave Camptosaurus an angry look

Cheeks concealed grinding teeth

Beak designed for cutting plant matter

Wide, long tail

Robust, powerful hind legs

Did You Know?

Camptosaurus means "bent lizard." It was given this name because of its hunched stance.

Very large eyes

Camptosaurus hatchling

Capable of walking on four legs and
running on two to evade predators

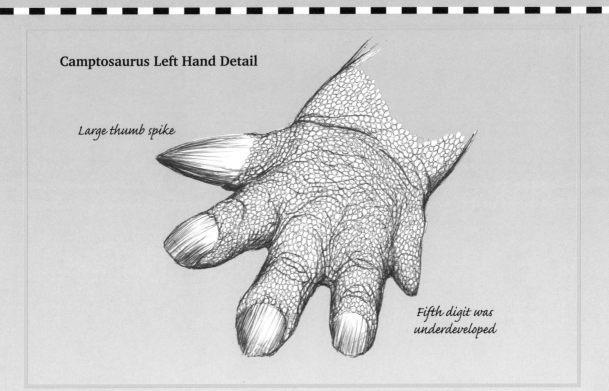

Camptosaurus Left Hand Detail

Large thumb spike

Fifth digit was underdeveloped

*Always alert for danger –
like many modern prey animals,
Camptosaurus juveniles gathered
around a parent for protection*

Late Jurassic Labyrinth

Help this Camptosaurus family find their way to food!

ANSWERS ON PAGE 158

What Am I?

Test your detective instincts as you figure out each sauropod and ornithischian below.
Find and place the matching stickers!

ANSWERS ON PAGE 158

Dino 1

I have spines running from my head to my tail and forward-facing, peg-like teeth. My long tail whips back and forth to keep predators at bay. What am I?

Place sticker here

Dino 2

I have a large dome on top of my head and I used to be known as a Brachiosaurus. I travel in packs with mostly juveniles weighing 1 ton or more. What am I?

Place sticker here

Dino 3

For many years, I went by the name, Apatosaurus. I can whip my long tail so fast that the tip makes a loud snapping sound. My gait is similar to that of a modern elephant. What am I?

Place sticker here

Dino 4

My name means "bent lizard" because I have a hunched stance. Shading above my eyes give me an angry look. I can walk on four legs or run on two to evade predators. What am I?

Place sticker here

Dino 5

I'm considered a medium-sized sauropod. I have a large head with a small dome on the top. My front feet are much smaller than my back feet, which hold most of my weight. What am I?

Place sticker here

Gargoyleosaurus parkpinorum

Location Observed: Wyoming, United States

Family: Nodosauridae

Length: 9 feet (3 meters)

Height: 3 feet (1 meter)

Weight: 600 pounds

Temperament: Defensive, aggressive

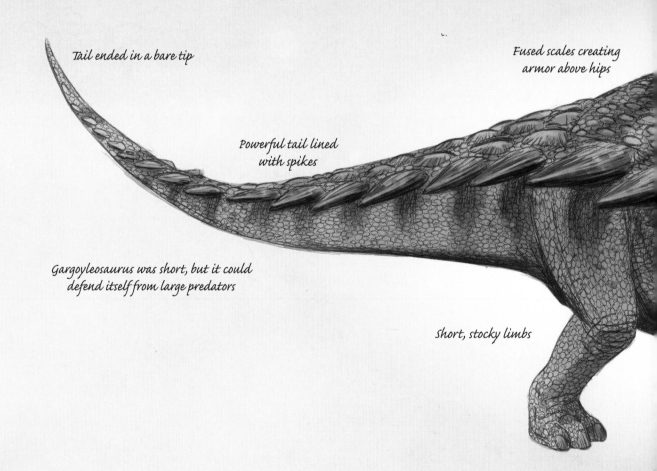

Tail ended in a bare tip

Fused scales creating armor above hips

Powerful tail lined with spikes

Gargoyleosaurus was short, but it could defend itself from large predators

Short, stocky limbs

Fused scales to top
of head

Horns above and below eyes

Small teeth

Triangular-shaped head

Thick scutes formed an
armored shell

Long spikes on sides
protected from attack

sharp bony spikes lined
both sides of the tail

Did You Know?

Wielded like an ax,
Gargoyleosaurus' tail was
designed to inflict harm to
any attacker.

Gargoyleosaurus' tail

Its hardened, dome-shaped
carapace was impenetrable

With a wide stance and a low center of gravity,
Gargoyleosaurus was very difficult to overturn

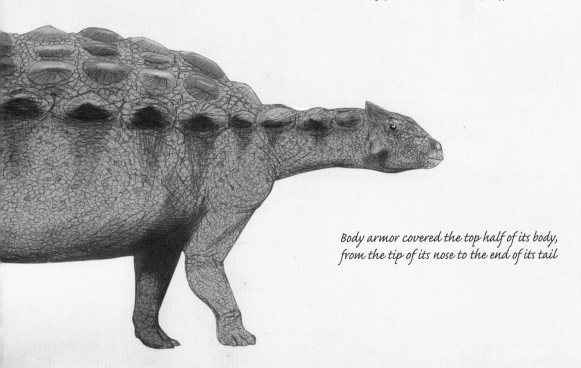

Body armor covered the top half of its body,
from the tip of its nose to the end of its tail

Long, rectangular head

Beak designed for cutting low-lying plants

Grinding teeth behind cheeks

Seven rows of flat plates along neck and back

Small head

Relatively long neck

Short forelimbs

Enormous spikes protruding from shoulders

Large hind limbs

Kentrosaurus aethiopicus

Location Observed: _Tanzania, Africa_

Family: _Stegosauridae_

Length: _13 feet (4 meters)_

Height: _5 feet (1.5 meters)_

Weight: _1,500 pounds_

Temperament: _Defensive, aggressive_

Seven rows of long spikes from mid-back to end of tail

Long, thick tail

Did You Know?

Kentrosaurus was much smaller than its American cousin, Stegosaurus.

True or False?

It is believed that ornithischians were shy and cautious.

ANSWER ON
PAGE 158

115

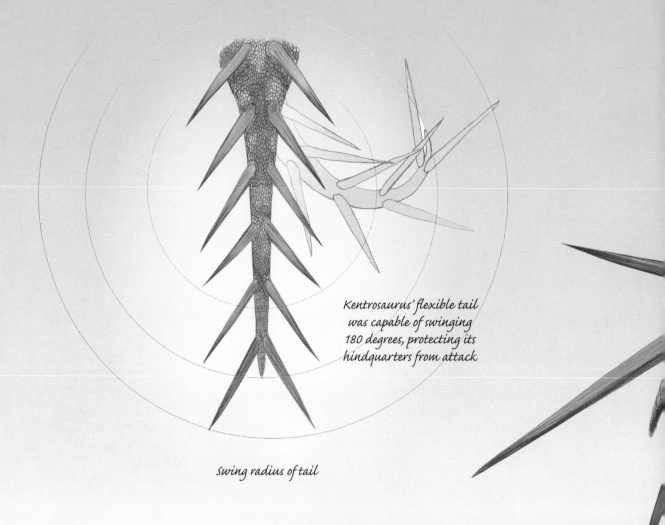

Kentrosaurus' flexible tail was capable of swinging 180 degrees, protecting its hindquarters from attack

swing radius of tail

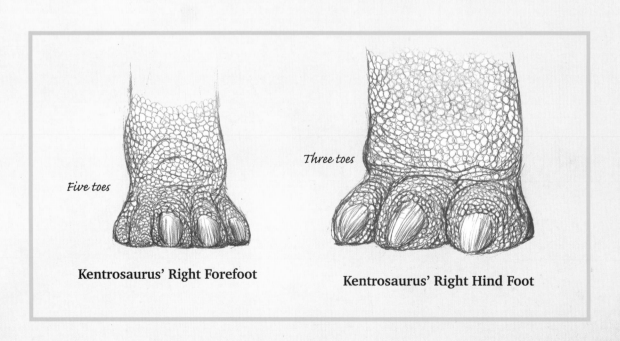

Five toes

Three toes

Kentrosaurus' Right Forefoot

Kentrosaurus' Right Hind Foot

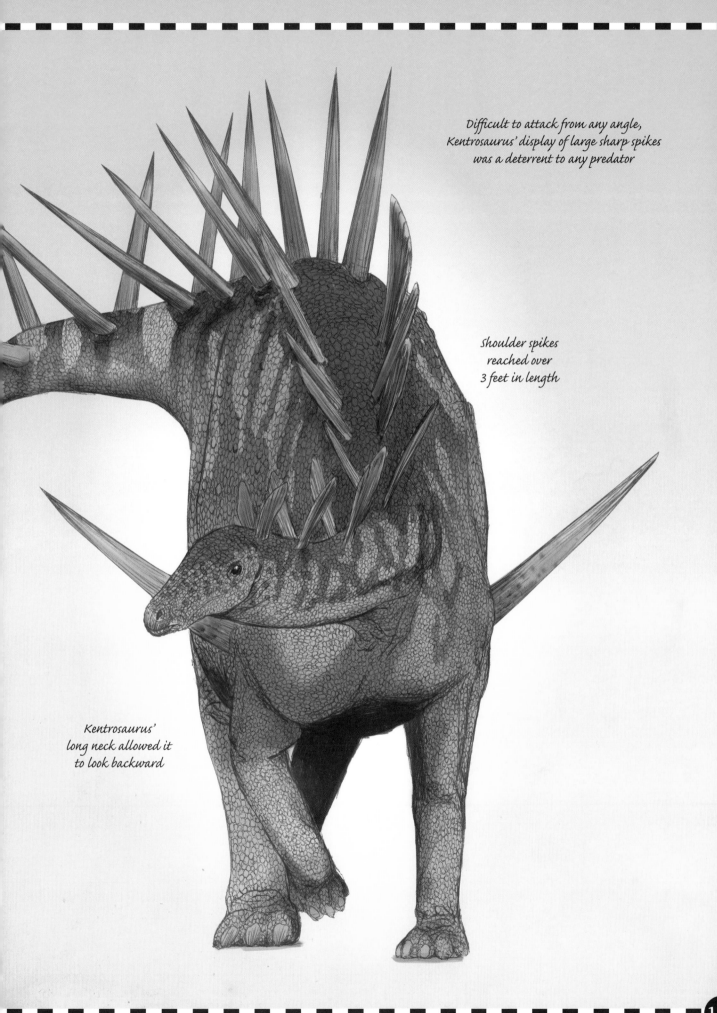

Difficult to attack from any angle,
Kentrosaurus' display of large sharp spikes
was a deterrent to any predator

shoulder spikes
reached over
3 feet in length

Kentrosaurus'
long neck allowed it
to look backward

Dino Grid Drawing

Learn how to draw a Camptosaurus and a Kentrosaurus using the grid method of drawing!
First turn your book so you see the dinosaurs upright. The use the blank grids on page 119
to copy what you see in each square below. Start with a sketch, and then give the dinosaurs
color with markers, colored pencils, or crayons!

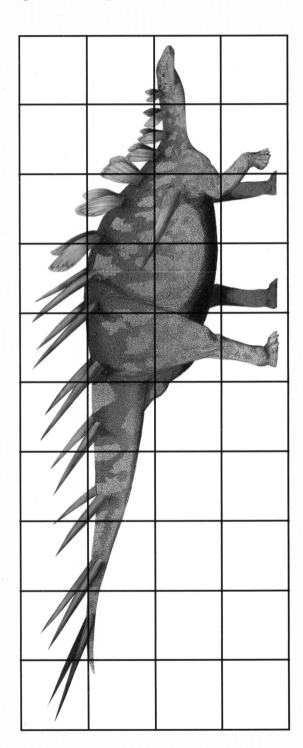

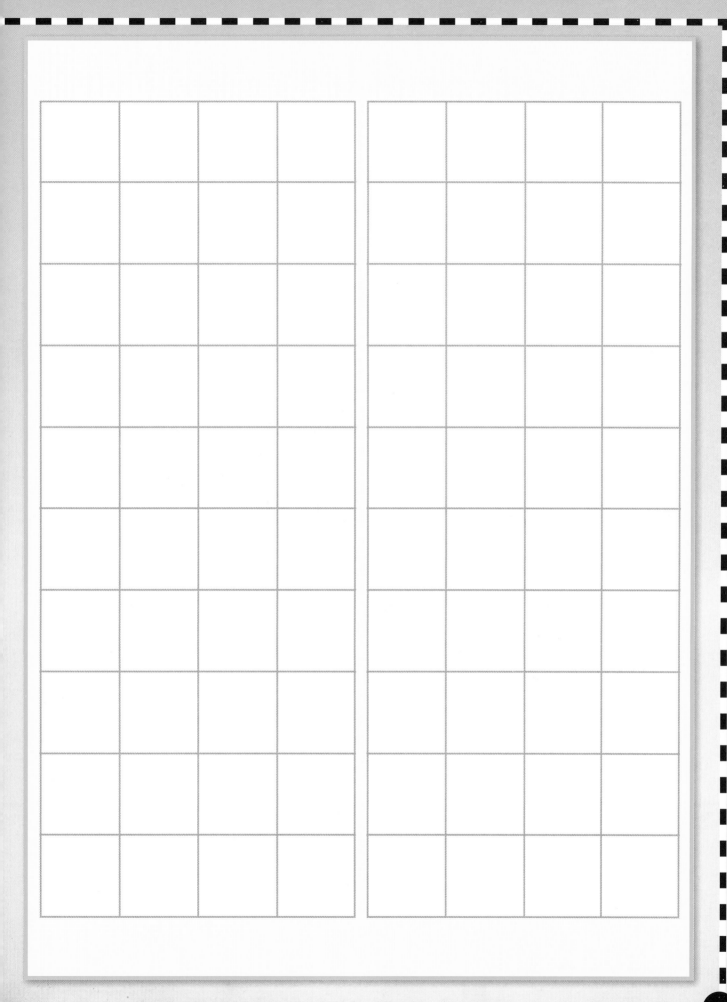

Stegosaurus stenops

Location Observed: *Colorado, United States*

Family: *Stegosauridae*

Length: *21 feet (6.5 meters)*

Height: *12 feet (3.5 meters)*

Weight: *3.5 tons*

Temperament: *Aggressive*

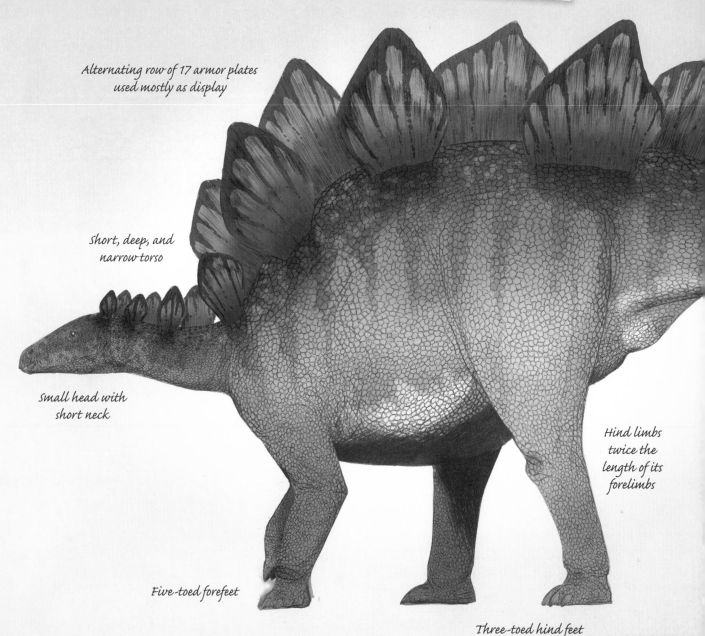

Alternating row of 17 armor plates used mostly as display

Short, deep, and narrow torso

Small head with short neck

Hind limbs twice the length of its forelimbs

Five-toed forefeet

Three-toed hind feet

Long, narrow head

Small teeth line
the sides of jaws

Thick, bony scales served as
protective armor around neck

Four tail spikes used
for defense

Muscular and deep tail

**True or
False?**
The Stegosaurus was
much larger than
its cousin, the
Kentrosaurus.

ANSWER ON
PAGE 158

A healthy adult Stegosaurus had few enemies. Its size, weight, and spiked tail made any predator think twice.

Stegosaurus was a large and extremely dangerous dinosaur

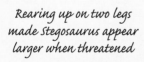

Rearing up on two legs made Stegosaurus appear larger when threatened

Four long tail spikes at the end of a powerful and flexible tail could easily kill any predator

Stegosaurus' Tail Detail

Did You Know?

Hatchling and juvenile Stegosaurus found security and protection from predators by staying close to adults.

At a couple of years old, juvenile Stegosaurus reached 5 feet in length and already had tail spikes

Coloring activity

Use markers, colored pencils, or crayons to color these dinosaurs!

Dino Races

Which dinosaur do you think would win in a race: the Diplodocus, the Stegosaurus, the Allosaurus, or the Compsognathus? Follow the lines to see who wins!

ANSWERS ON PAGE 158

Where in the World?

This map shows where these ornithischian fossils has been found.
Place the dino sticker in the corresponding box!

ANSWERS ON PAGE 158

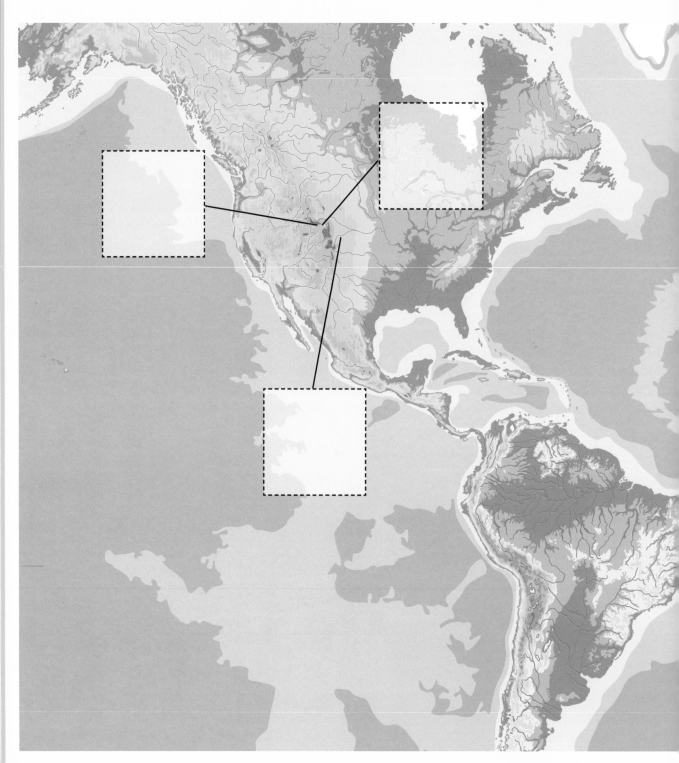

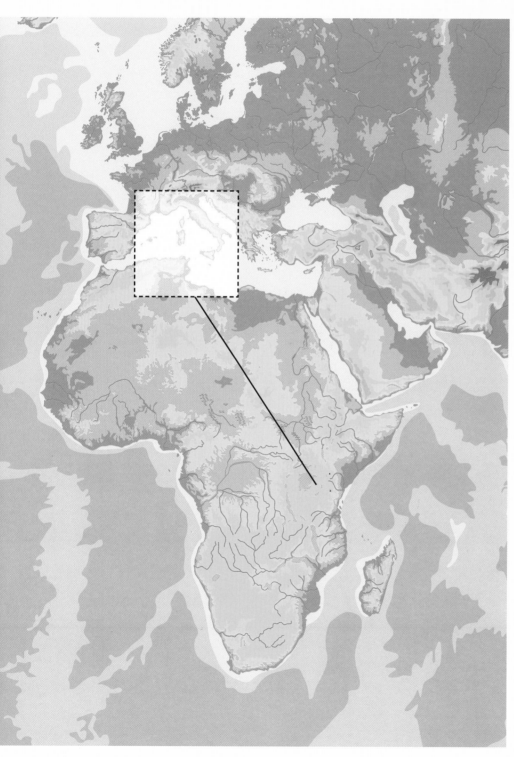

☐ Camptosaurus
dispar

☐ Gargoyleosaurus
parkpinorum

☐ Kentrosaurus
aethiopicus

☐ Stegosaurus
stenops

Dino Sudoku

Solve these sudoku puzzles using the symbols below. Remember: A symbol can only appear once in each column, row, and box (2 x 2 squares).

Good luck!

ANSWERS ON PAGE 159

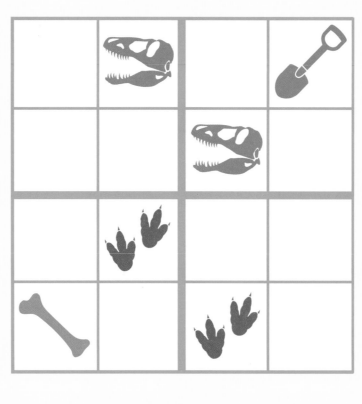

Silhouette Match-up

You've learned about all the dinosaurs below. Can you match each silhouette to its name?
Try it without peeking first!

ANSWERS ON PAGE 159

A. Brontosaurus louisae

B. Kentrosaurus aethiopicus

C. Compsognathus longipes

D. Stegosaurus stenops

E. Allosaurus fragilis

F. Diplodocus hallorum

Pterosaurs

It's late afternoon, almost dusk, as the sun begins to approach the Jurassic horizon. The evening will be a welcome relief as the sun takes its relentless heat with it as it sets. The day's end signals the arrival of new animals, as well as a new look to the landscape. The last rays of the sun's light accent the millions of insects dotting the air, almost like a cloud. There are mayflies, mosquitoes, damselflies, and dragonflies all moving at different speeds, slowly stirring the cloud they form. With long slashes, larger flying animals begin to cut through the air like a knife. There are dozens of them all feeding on the assortment of insects floating before them. They consist of two body types: one is larger with a pointed beak and tail ending in a diamond-shaped rudder; the other is much smaller with a rounded head.

With effortless precision, they pierce the air and snap up their prey, zigzagging and narrowly missing one another as if they've rehearsed this intricate dance. The largest of them has a wingspan about the size of an eagle, while the smallest species is no bigger than a blue jay. One swoops inches from your head as you feel the wind rush past you and hear the quick flapping of its wings. You are an eyewitness to the daily feast of the pterosaurs: the absolute masters of flight during the Late Jurassic.

The pterosaurs flew using the same principles modern birds use today, with wings made from a fibrous membrane extending from their elongated fourth fingers and attached to their hind limbs. Pterosaur skeletons were constructed of a strong framework of hollow bones, with skulls containing openings called "fenestra," which reduced weight without sacrificing structural support. They were truly a masterpiece of engineering.

Did You Know?

Pterosaurs' anatomy was very efficient for flight. Its skeleton included a system of air sacs that worked with the lungs to aid in respiration and reduce body weight.

Pterosaurs of the Late Jurassic

By the Late Jurassic, pterosaurs had evolved specialized adaptations for hunting and flight. Species like *Rhamphorhynchus muensteri* were equipped with thin, forward-facing teeth to spear insects and fish in mid-flight. Its curved beak also had sharp tips on both the skull and jaw that ensured prey didn't escape. Rhamphorhynchus was also known for its long, rigid tail, which it used as a counterbalance, much like the tail of a kite. By swinging its tail, it could change direction and control its flight at will. *Anurognathus ammoni*, by comparison, flew without the aid of a long tail for balance. Its long, slender wings and rounded frog-like face were more suited for flying in tighter quarters between trees and obstacles where it too hunted for insects in midair. Anurognathus also had large, evolved eyes to allow for vision in low-light conditions, making it an excellent nocturnal hunter.

These two species set the wheels of evolution in motion for what would later become the flying giants of the Cretaceous. In the following pages, take a closer look at two of the rulers of the Late Jurassic skies.

Dino Decoding

What does the word "pterosaur" mean in ancient Greek?
Use the alphabet key on page 18 to decode the answer!
ANSWER ON PAGE 159

___ ___ ___ ___ ___ ___   ___ ___ ___ ___ ___ ___
 <   &   =   ~   5 $ *   &   #   @   ? $

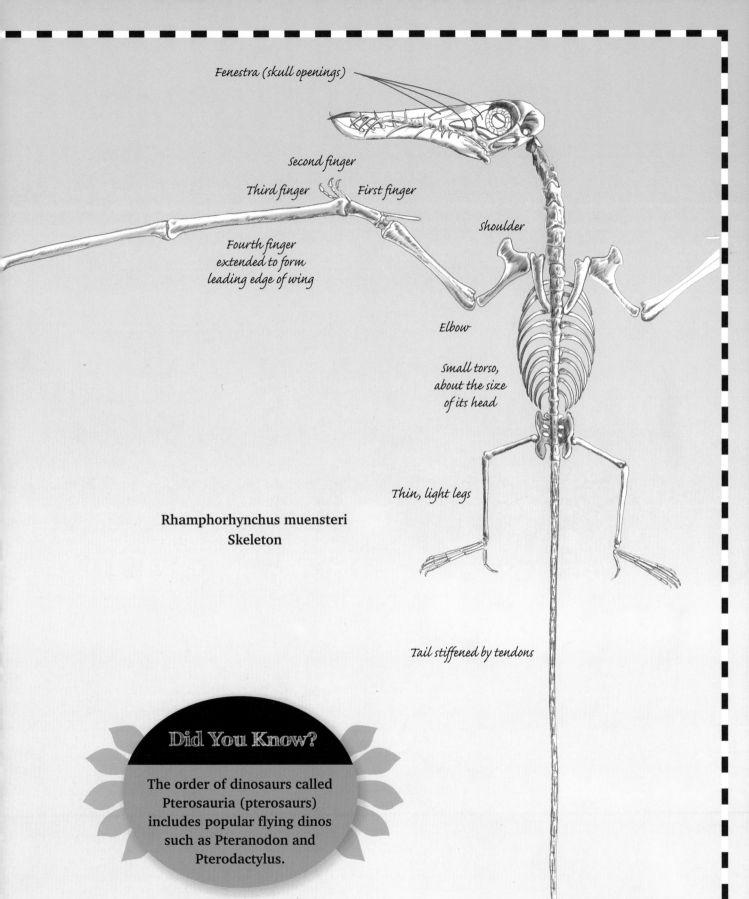

Fenestra (skull openings)

Second finger

Third finger   First finger

Fourth finger
extended to form
leading edge of wing

Shoulder

Elbow

Small torso,
about the size
of its head

Rhamphorhynchus muensteri
Skeleton

Thin, light legs

Tail stiffened by tendons

Did You Know?

The order of dinosaurs called
Pterosauria (pterosaurs)
includes popular flying dinos
such as Pteranodon and
Pterodactylus.

Flight of the Pterosaur

Help this Anurognathus maneuver its way to the center of this maze,
where it'll find a cloud of insects to eat!

ANSWER ON PAGE 159

Pterosaur Word Search

As you continue to learn about pterosaurs, remember these key words! They are also buried in the word search below. Can you find them all?

ANSWERS ON PAGE 159

- ☐ Anurognathus
- ☐ Fenestra
- ☐ Hollow bones
- ☐ Hunters
- ☐ Insects
- ☐ Large eyes
- ☐ Membranes
- ☐ Rhamphorhynchus
- ☐ Webbing
- ☐ Wings

```
H L Y J I N P Q P S S R R O I Z P O K F
O O Z V Y L S O C F V V C A K L G O U Q
L G K J H Z S W H Q E X F N O A B H P K
L G Q O F F B I V J L Q D U A R R B R D
O R V H X X U X S Z Y M O R Q G V B T Z
W P H K C N F T K Z P V D O Z E X E P Q
B F H A K V X V F R E C Q G H E Z U J I
O Y E K M D N F U E H I G N Q Y Q H X N
N Y O N R P N M M Q E U Z A J E O D M S
E K V B E L H E A L Y I A T B S P S O E
S W Q L A S F O D J S W K H L J D V T C
B V L F G N T E R C Y L C U Z S G B R T
I X V Q A P G R L H H Q E S N J V J G S
W M N N I W U I A B Y L M X Z W X S P S
H Z F U H J G A O H Y N W E B B I N G X
S B O S M Z I I V D V C C M L C R P N W
P M E M B R A N E S M R R H K J P C Y S
P E C H Y N P Y K P M V L G U O D X D Z
H U N T E R S N V Z F D Q L H S J I G X
Q J L I D Y V I J M O W S H W I N G S V
```

Anurognathus ammoni

Location Observed: *Germany*

Family: *Anurognathidae*

Length: *6 inches (.15 meter)*

Height: *20 inches (0.5 meter) wingspan*

Weight: *5 grams*

Temperament: *Elusive*

Very short, round face

Wide mouth

Large eyes for nocturnal hunting

Three-fingered hands

Head, neck, and torso
were covered in thin
hair-like fibers

Thin, pin-like teeth
designed for catching
insects midair

Short tail

Curved claws
on feet

Did You Know?

Anurognathus is one of the smallest
pterosaurs ever discovered. Pterosaurs
from the later Cretaceous period
were much larger, especially the
Quetzalcoatlus. This giant flier
was as large as a giraffe!

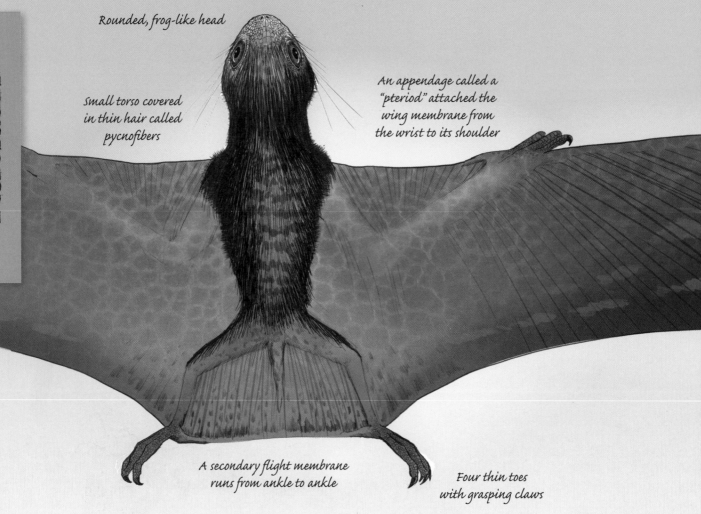

Rounded, frog-like head

An appendage called a "pteriod" attached the wing membrane from the wrist to its shoulder

Small torso covered in thin hair called pycnofibers

A secondary flight membrane runs from ankle to ankle

Four thin toes with grasping claws

Word Scramble

How does an Anurognathus take flight? Unscramble the words below to finish the fact!

ANSWER ON PAGE 159

Using its strong muscles, Anurognathus launched itself into the air by leaping forward and

— — — — — — — — — — — — — — —
N I H P G U S   F O F   H W T I

— — — — — — — — — — — —.
T I S   M E B O R F I L S.

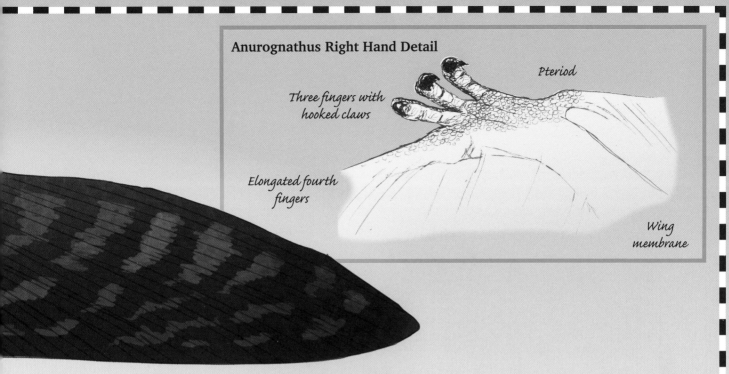

Anurognathus Right Hand Detail

Three fingers with hooked claws

Elongated fourth fingers

Pteriod

Wing membrane

Long, thin, and fibrous filaments at ends of wings added strength and flexibility

Using its strong muscles, Anurognathus launched itself into the air by leaping forward and pushing off with its forelimbs

Rhamphorhynchus muensteri

Location Observed: *Germany*

Family: *Rhamphorhynchidae*

Length: *4 feet (1.26 meters)*

Height: *5 feet, 9 inches (1.81 meters) wingspan*

Weight: *2.5 pounds*

Temperament: *Reclusive, shy*

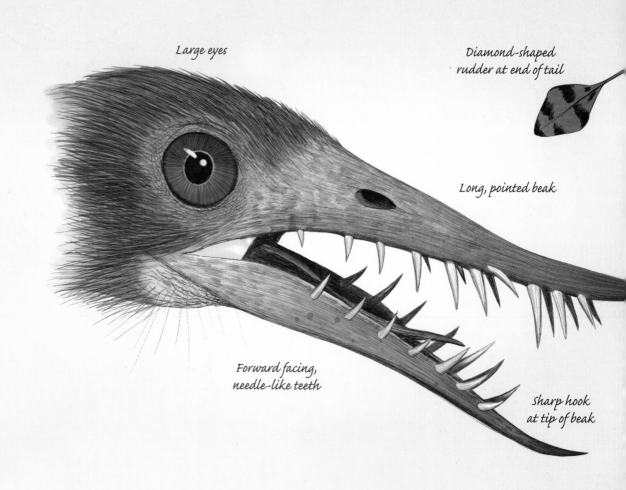

Large eyes

Diamond-shaped
rudder at end of tail

Long, pointed beak

Forward facing,
needle-like teeth

Sharp hook
at tip of beak

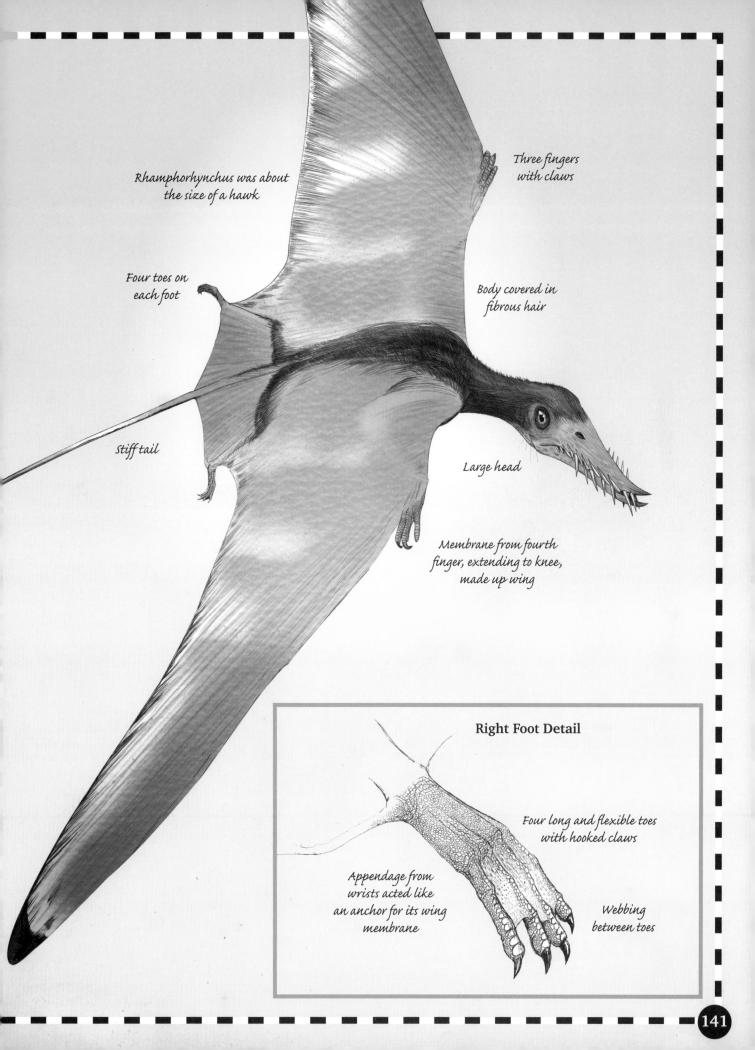

Rhamphorhynchus was about the size of a hawk

Three fingers with claws

Four toes on each foot

Body covered in fibrous hair

Stiff tail

Large head

Membrane from fourth finger, extending to knee, made up wing

Right Foot Detail

Four long and flexible toes with hooked claws

Appendage from wrists acted like an anchor for its wing membrane

Webbing between toes

Draw a Rhamphorhynchus

On land, Rhamphorhynchus walked on all four limbs by folding its wings back, causing its hands and feet to make contact with the ground. Use the blank grid below to copy what you see in each square below. Start with a sketch, and then give it color with markers, colored pencils, or crayons!

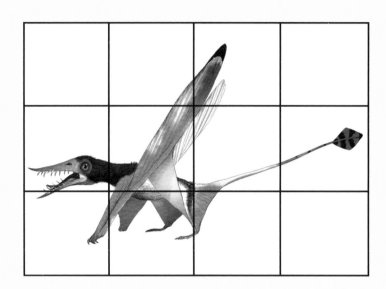

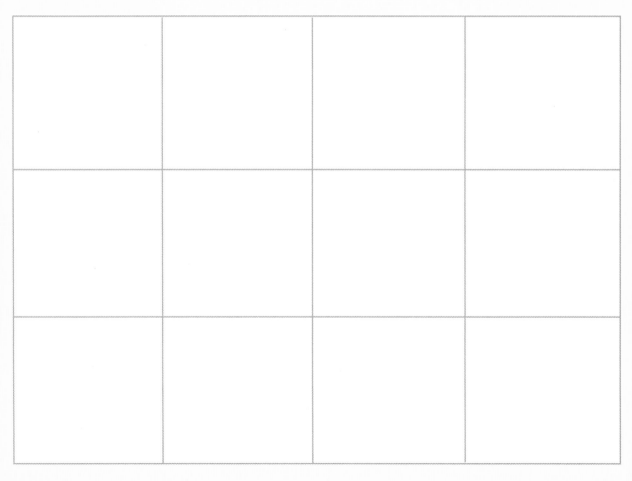

Did You Know?

Pterosaurs were the first vertebrates to evolve self-sufficient fight millions of years before mammals (bats) or even birds.

Opportunistic in nature, no catch goes unchallenged

Rhamphorhynchus fed mostly on fish, but was also known to eat small flying insects

By spreading its legs, Rhamphorhynchus created a broad surface area for its wings

Rhamphorhynchus' long, rigid tail acted like a counterbalance, allowing it to effortlessly change direction midair

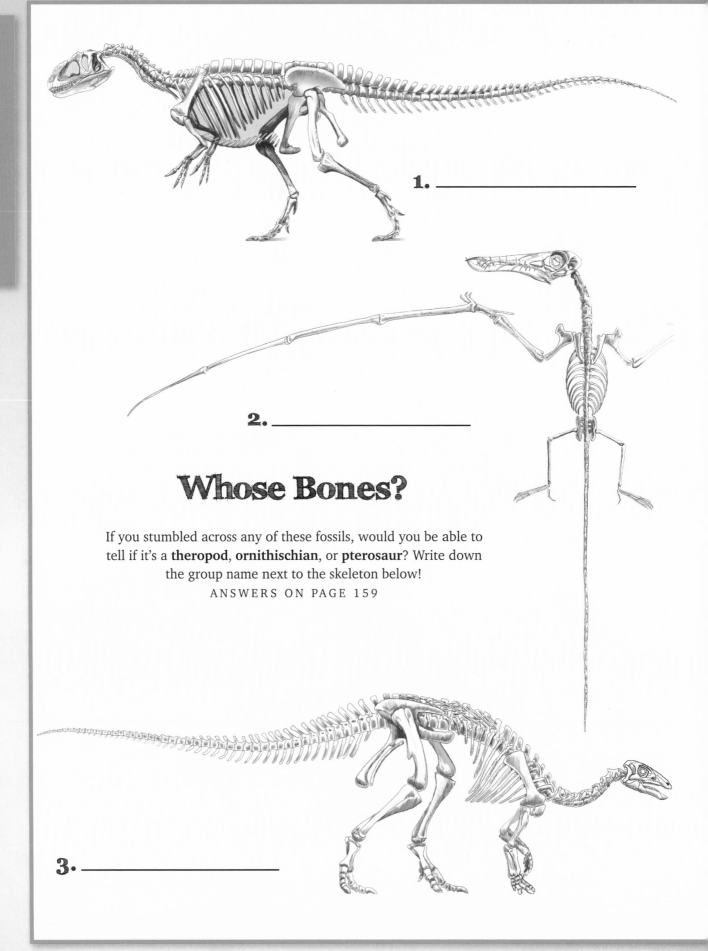

1. _____

2. _____

Whose Bones?

If you stumbled across any of these fossils, would you be able to tell if it's a **theropod**, **ornithischian**, or **pterosaur**? Write down the group name next to the skeleton below!

ANSWERS ON PAGE 159

3. _____

Draw a line to match the dinosaur to its skull!

ANSWERS ON PAGE 159

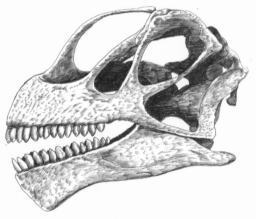

Mammals

It's another typical day in the Late Jurassic, hot and steamy with the constant harassment of biting insects. You escape into the shade of a grove to avoid the sun, and you are surprised to see the trees alive with movement. Jumping from branch to branch, there are several small animals with long tails interacting playfully. They look like a mixture of a squirrel and an opossum and act very much like modern-day mammals. They have total command of the trees where they feel at home, oblivious to any of the dangers that come with living on the ground. These animals are a startling contrast to the other wildlife experienced in the Jurassic. Watching them almost makes you forget you are 150 million years away from the Earth you know. These are the early mammals, your great ancestors, and a glimpse of what evolution has in store for the Earth.

The first true mammals began to appear around the Late Triassic period, about 50 to 75 million years before the Late Jurassic. They evolved alongside the dinosaurs, but remained small, carving out evolutionary niches and not competing directly with them. Their small size was a blessing in disguise, as it allowed them to survive past the extinction event that killed off the dinosaurs around 65 million years ago. Afterwards, the mammals would flourish and slowly begin to evolve into larger species, giving rise to early primates and ultimately humans.

Mammals of the Late Jurassic

By the Late Jurassic, mammals adapted to different lifestyles, including species like *Fruitafossor windscheffeli*, which developed specialized traits designed for digging and eating termites and ants. Others like *Castorocauda lutrasimilis* made the water their home by evolving the attributes necessary for a semi-aquatic life, one similar to a modern-day otter.

In this section, we will take a look at two well-documented species: *Shenshou lui*, an arboreal or "tree-dwelling" animal from China, and *Juramaia sinensis*, also from China. Shenshou evolved hands and feet with opposable fingers perfect for grasping branches and a prehensile tail capable of gripping onto trees and acting like a fifth limb. Juramaia is equally at home in the trees as on the ground and is built more like a small mouse or shrew. What makes Juramaia notable is that it is considered to be the first placental mammal, meaning it gave birth to live young which developed in a womb. These are two of the early mammals who lived among dinosaurs and foreshadow the evolutionary changes the earth is soon to experience.

Dino Decoding

What word describes the process of animals adapting to their environment over time?
Use the alphabet key on page 18 to decode the answer!
ANSWER ON PAGE 159

$$\overline{5}\ \overline{6}\ \overline{-}\ \overline{*}\ \overline{>}\ \overline{2}\ \overline{\&}\ \overline{-}\ \overline{=}$$

Shenshou lui

Location Observed: *Liaoning, China*

Family: *Mammalia*

Length: *1 foot (0.3 meter)*

Weight: *10 ounces*

Temperament: *Cautious*

Large eyes allowed
shenshou to see in low-
light conditions

Very large incisors

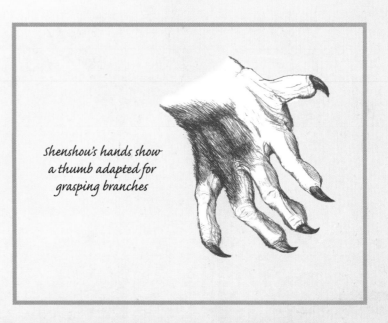

Shenshou's hands show
a thumb adapted for
grasping branches

About the size of a squirrel

Shenshou lived almost exclusively in trees and were omnivorous, eating insects, nuts, and fruit

Did You Know?

The Jurassic period was named after the Jura Mountains between Switzerland and France, which contain rocks formed during this era.

Long, prehensile tail

Juramaia sinensis

Location Observed: Liaoning, China

Family: Mammalia

Length: 5 inches (0.12 meter)

Weight: 15 grams

Temperament: Reclusive, shy

About the size
of a shrew

Long tail
covered in hair

Feet designed for both
climbing and running on
the ground

Dino Decoding

Do you know what "Juramaia" means? Use the alphabet key on page 18 to decode the answer!

ANSWER ON PAGE 159

) > ? @ / / & 9   + - 2 ^ 5 ?

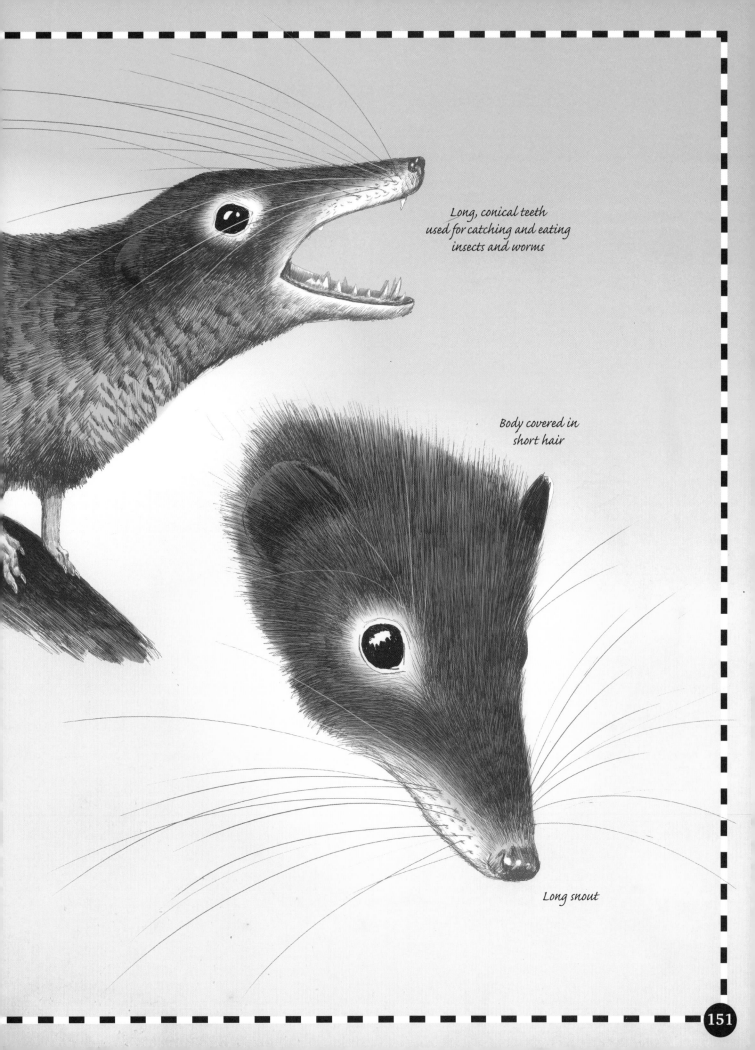

Long, conical teeth
used for catching and eating
insects and worms

Body covered in
short hair

Long snout

A-maze-ing Mammals

Help the Juramaia scurry its way through a maze.
A tasty worm awaits!

ANSWER ON PAGE 159

Test Your Memory

The mammals of the Late Jurassic were the closest relatives to human beings at that time! Answer the questions below and see what you can remember about our great ancestors.

ANSWERS ON PAGE 159

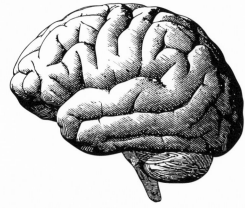

1. Which of the following is NOT a characteristic of Late Jurassic mammals?

    A. A long tail

    B. A large body size

    C. Large eyes

    D. Grasping hands and feet

2. Unscramble the word! Early mammals were well equipped for living in the ____ ____ ____ ____ ____.

      e   s   t   e   r

3. True or false? Most mammals lay eggs. _____

4. Instead of scales or feathers, early mammals were covered in _____.

Me-a-saur Personality Quiz

Answer the questions below and discover what kind of dino you're most like:
a theropod, sauropod, or pterosaur!

ANSWERS ON PAGE 159

1. Which of the following describes you best?

A. I may not be fast, but I'm very tall!

B. I'm strong and fast.

C. I'm small and graceful.

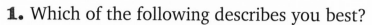

2. What is your favorite type of meal?

A. I'll take a large salad, please.

B. There's nothing like a big, juicy steak!

C. I prefer lots of small snacks throughout the day.

3. Which statement best describes your social life?

A. I enjoy relaxing with friends.

B. I'm not afraid of anyone. In fact, I'm rough and tough.

C. I'm pretty shy, so I don't mind being alone.

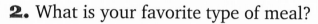

4. What's your favorite way to travel?

A. Walking or biking is just fine for me.

B. In a sports car. Is there any other way?

C. Planes, please!

Notes from My Prehistoric Journey

Fill in the blanks to record
your Late Jurassic favorites!
Remember: There are no
wrong answers.

My all-time favorite
Jurassic animal:

_____

_____

The strangest-looking
dinosaur:

_____

_____

The scariest dinosaur:

_____

_____

The most fascinating
dinosaur:

_____

_____

Dinosaur fossils that I've
seen in person:

_____

_____

Dinosaur fossils that I'd
like to see someday:

_____

_____

_____

_____

Dinosaurs I want to
learn more about:

_____

_____

_____

_____

Answer Key

Page 17

	2	3	4	2	2
	1	7	3	9	3
1	2	2	3	1	4	8
4	3	4	4	5	6	5
5	1	10	7	6	9	10
7	2	1	8	4		
10	4	6	9	10		

Page 18
Terrible Lizard

Page 19

```
H P T I L I Z G Q V N A Y L I B Q C W Y
S U Z D O G V I V F M D W Y U I A D D W
Z N N J D B E G F T D A N H Y R I Y E A
G Z E T S H T A P K K P K N Q I O U V I
U W C B E O U N F L R T T W C F T J O Z
M S A C M R B T P N B A Y X F P S J L H
K G V A O Y C I H N R T J C D S Y S U V
Q Z U R R J D S I D A I S O M B J H T O
B W H N W Y K M E J W O E P U Y L A I G
I L A I X T N D W N F N U F U D G R O Y
P P W V N L R G A E V S G P S V F O N O
E E N O H E U H I Z J A W K W W R T X Q
D I D R H J J M D R M T V M F Z J E B S
A W J O X F X B L H E M U E M E Z E I K
L T N U W T P R E D A T O R A L V T E J
X Z G S W S H D I Z I Y J V T C N H R A
D Y E S Y J F U B L S H Y E V K W T G I
K Z D U T A Q V E K E V T N E L V B R X
D S C A L E S M B F C W B Y N Q N E C D
Y C L A W S A V E R A M U X N R Z F H J
```

Page 22
True! Dinosaur skulls are very delicate, which makes them a very rare find for paleontologists.

Page 29
Missing Link

Page 35
False! Ceratosaurus had a row of bony armor, called osteoderms, along its back for protection. This was a rare adaptation for a carnivore!

Page 39
Chicken

Page 44

Page 45
Tyrannosaurus Rex

Page 49

Page 52
Apex Predator

Page 55
☐ Yangchuanosaurus lived a solitary life and hunted alone.
☑ Yangchuanosaurus is closely related to Allosaurus.
☐ Yangchuanosaurus was a very slow runner.

Page 56

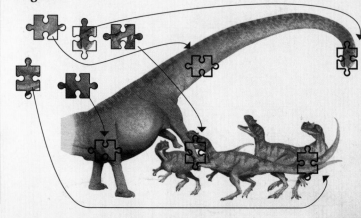

Page 61

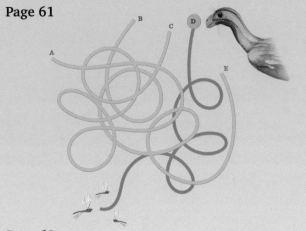

Page 62

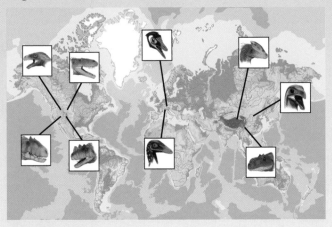

Page 64
Coprolite

Page 65
Dino 1: Archaeopteryx
Dino 2: Torvosaurus
Dino 3: Ornitholestes
Dino 4: Ceratosaurus
Dino 5: Yi qi

Page 72

Page 73

```
P H G U M V L T M Y A A O C V W P  B K Z
C L E Y L E H H G G L N Z Q N U R  R H N
T T I A L R D K G V P N L U J J E  A L E
P K H Y V J T L K X R F Q A V Q C  C L X
C X T E Y Y B R S S H I U D T M O  H G F
N A H W E Q T N H U R M K R A R C  I O M
R G M P B R R A C T D K C O T U I  O M T
D G N A K D A O I B O D W P J C A  S E W
Q W O R R Y Z O X L R C O E S D L  A V P
V N A N J A K L F R S F T D O E I  U C O
G R A C T D S K V G Y E Z A H J J  R G W
Y D P N E L Q A N J I L L N J S I  Q N
J N E P J M E C U L W A Y S B Z F  D K K
B K L B O T X D G R W R N F L C U  A C F
Y O W S N E Y L M K I Y D T F A P  E A X
E M T F O U H N L G M D K P S E A  J S D
D I P L O D O C I D A E A N S C Z  R O J
S Q Y C U V T Z R D V E I E U U Z  K I Q
P H U L W G Y O O W P R B L J M W  M R Z
L O N G N E C K G P L A N T E A T E R A
```

Page 74

Page 75
Test Your Memory
3: Jurassic Period
1: Permian Period
4: Cretaceous Period
2: Triassic Period

Guess Who?

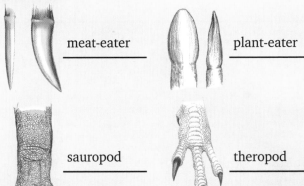

meat-eater _____   plant-eater _____

sauropod _____   theropod _____

Page 77
Thunder Lizard

Page 95

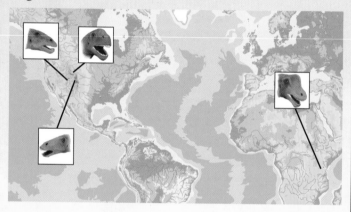

1	2	78	28	80	48	98
79	3	4	5	6	58	90
1	4	3	27	7	29	30
31	32	33	34	5	6	7	8	39	40
41	42	43	44	45	46	47	9	49	50
88	26	53	14	13	12	11	10	59	60
61	62	63	15	14	66	67	68	69	70
74	72	73	16	15	18	77
81	82	83	17	16	19	20
91	64	93	18	19	20	21

Page 96

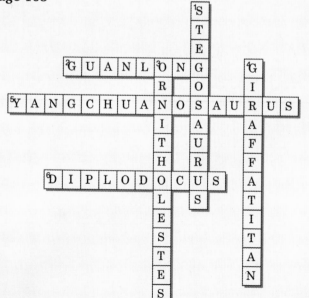

Page 103

Page 108

Page 109
Dino 1: Diplodocus
Dino 2: Giraffatitan
Dino 3: Brontosaurus
Dino 4: Camptosaurus
Dino 5: Camarasaurus

Page 115
False! Scientists believe that many ornithischians were aggressive.

Page 121
True! Stegosaurus was much larger than the Kentrosaurus.

Page 125
1st place: Compsognathus
2nd place: Allosaurus
3rd place: Diplodocus
4th place: Stegosaurus

Page 126

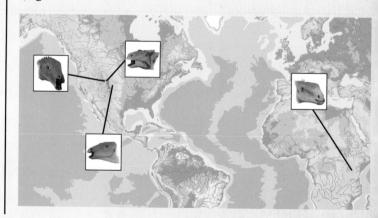

Page 128

Page 129

Page 132

Winged Lizard

Page 134

Page 135

Page 138

Using its strong muscles, Anurognathus launched itself into the air by leaping forward and <u>pushing off with its forelimbs</u>.

Page 144

1. theropod
2. pterosaur
3. ornithischian

Page 145

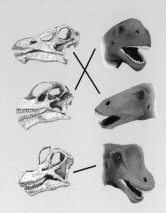

Page 147

Evolution

Page 150

Jurassic Mother

Page 152

Page 153

1. B
2. trees
3. False
4. hair

Page 154

1. Mostly As: Slow and steady, you're most like a sauropod.
2. Mostly Bs: No bones about it, you're like a theropod.
3. Mostly Cs: Small, graceful, and shy, you're most like a pterosaur.

Pronunciation Key

Theropods (Theer-uh-pods)

Allosaurus fragilis (Al-oh-sore-us, fraj-ill-iss)

Archaeopteryx lithographica (Are-key-op-trex, lith-o-graf-e-ka)

Ceratosaurus nasicornis (Sir-at-toe-sore-us, nay-si-corn-iss)

Compsognathus longipes (Comp-sog-nay-thus, long-gipes)

Guanlong wucaii (Ga-wan-long, goo-kai)

Ornitholestes hermanni (Or-nith-oh-less-teaze, her-man-knee)

Torvosaurus tanneri (Tor-vo-sore-us, tan-nery)

Yangchuanosaurus shangyouensis (Yan-chwahn-oh-sore-us, shang-u-en-sis)

Yi qi (Ee-chee)

Sauropods (Sore-uh-pods)

Brontosaurus louisae (Bron-toe-sore-us, louise-ay)

Camarasaurus supremus (Kam-ara-sore-us, sue-preme-us)

Diplodocus hallorum (Di-plod-oh-kus, hall-ore-um)

Giraffatitan brancai (Ji-raf-a-tie-tan, bran-kai)

Ornithischians (Ore-ni-thisk-key-ahns)

Camptosaurus dispar (Kamp-toe-sore-us, dis-par)

Gargoyleosaurus parkpinorum (Gar-goy-lo-sore-us, park-pin-ore-um)

Kentrosaurus aethiopicus (Ken-tro-sore-us, ethi-opee-cus)

Stegosaurus stenops (Steg-go-sore-us, sten-opps)

Pterosaurs (Ter-uh-sore)

Anurognathus ammoni (An-your-og-nath-us, am-mon-i)

Rhamphorhynchus muensteri (Ram-for-ink-uss, moon-stery)

Mammals

Shenshou lui (Shen-shoe, le-oh)

Juramaia sinensis (Joor-ah-my-ah, sin-n-sis)

Stickers

Page 62

Allosaurus
fragilis

Archaeopteryx
lithographica

Ceratosaurus
nasicornis

Compsognathus
longipes

Guanlong
wucaii

Ornitholestes
hermanni

Torvosaurus
tanneri

Yangchuanosaurus
shangyouensis

Yi qi

Page 65

 Ceratosaurus

 Yi qi

 Archaeopteryx

 Ornitholestes

Torvosaurus

Page 96

Brontosaurus
louisae

Camarasaurus
supremus

Diplodocus
hallorum

Giraffatitan
brancai

Page 109

Giraffatitan

Brontosaurus

Diplodocus

Camarasaurus

Camptosaurus

Page 126

Camptosaurus
dispar

Gargoyleosaurus
parkpinorum

Kentrosaurus
aethiopicus

Stegosaurus
stenops

nathus

Shenshou lui

ia Activity Journals

ASSIC

MALS

Rhamphorhynchus

Ornitholestes

Camptosaurus

Allosaurus

Guanlong

Gargoyleosaurus

Ornitholestes

Camarasaurus

Kentrosaurus

Yi qi

Comp.

Animal Encyclope

JUR
ANI

Guanlong

Anurognathus

Stegosaurus